The Reference Shelf™

Warfare in the 21st Century

Edited by Jeremy K. Brown

The Reference Shelf
Volume 75 • Number 3

The H. W. Wilson Company
2003

The Reference Shelf

The books in this series contain reprints of articles, excerpts from books, addresses on current issues, and studies of social trends in the United States and other countries. There are six separately bound numbers in each volume, all of which are usually published in the same calendar year. Numbers one through five are each devoted to a single subject, providing background information and discussion from various points of view and concluding with a subject index and comprehensive bibliography that lists books, pamphlets, and abstracts of additional articles on the subject. The final number of each volume is a collection of recent speeches, and it contains a cumulative speaker index. Books in the series may be purchased individually or on subscription.

Library of Congress has cataloged this title as follows:

Warfare in the 21st century / edited by Jeremy K. Brown.
    p. cm.— (The reference shelf; v. 75, no. 3)
    Includes bibliographical references and index.
    ISBN 0-8242-1021-2
    1. Military art and science. 2. Military history, Modern—21st century.
I. Brown, Jeremy K. II. Series.

U102.W279 2003
355.02'09'05—dc21

                                                            2003050171

Cover: Photo by Paul Edmondson (© Stone)

Visit H.W. Wilson's Web site: www.hwwilson.com

Printed in the United States of America

Contents

Preface

Warfare is as old a concept as humanity itself. From the Peloponnesian war to the 2003 conflict in Iraq, humankind has continued to fight for the causes it deems worthy. The United States alone has averaged a major conflict every 10–20 years since it was founded. As human beings grow in intelligence, so do they grow in their ability to wage war. With each successive conflict, they adopt new tools, new strategies and new approaches to the art of war. Now, at the dawn of a new century, humankind is looking at something of a golden age of combat. Computer technology has become an indispensable tool in warfare, plotting troop movements and relaying attack plans and other essential information to soldiers via satellite. Now more than ever, the world is seeing the marriage of the old and new methods of battle. Richard Marcinko, a former Navy SEAL with more than 30 years of special warfare experience, perhaps put it best, noting, "A trooper on the ground must assimilate into the dichotomy of riding horseback and calling in laser-guided weapons on a target."

Sun Tzu, the great military strategist, once said, "All war is deception," a statement that seems especially true today. In the fallout from the September 11, 2001, terrorist attacks, one immutable fact is clear: We are facing a new era of warfare. No longer will armies simply square off on a battlefield, charging at one another with bayonets flashing. Now the enemy skulks among us, ready to strike with homemade radiological weapons or biological agents like smallpox, anthrax, and tularemia. Overhead, pilotless "drones" seek out their targets with more precision and accuracy than any human pilot could attempt to master. Soldiers now train for urban warfare, preparing to fight door to door in the event of a terrorist invasion.

With a new era of warfare comes a new enemy. As the world learned on 9/11, attacks at home or abroad need not originate from trained military personnel but men and women with enough fanatical devotion to crash an airplane into a building. In order to face these new enemies, we must understand them. Today's soldiers must therefore undergo language training and, at the very least, be equipped with translating devices that can allow them to assimilate better into foreign cultures.

The first section, "Theaters of Modern War," shows how the battlefields of the 21st century range from scorching deserts to the virtual landscape of cyberspace. The second section of this book, "Terrorism," examines the face of the enemy the world is now fighting, as well as the motivations behind their actions. Section III, "Chemical and Biological Weapons," covers an insidious type of warfare, revealing how many biological agents remain unaccounted for after the collapse of the Soviet Union and what steps the world is taking to combat them. "Nuclear and Radiological Weapons," the book's fourth section, looks at a 60-year-old threat from a modern perspective. In addition to traditional tactical weapons, the section also discusses radiological weapons, such as dirty bombs, which can be assembled by spare parts from X-ray machines. Section V, titled "Non-lethal Weapons," covers a different side of war, one in which no one has to die. Weapons such as rubber bullets, stun guns, and sticky foam are reducing the number of casualties that normally result from combat. The final section, "The Future of Modern War," looks ahead to where and how the wars of tomorrow will be fought.

I would like to thank the publishers of periodicals throughout the world who generously gave their permission to have their articles reprinted in this book. I must also extend my gratitude to all those at the H.W. Wilson Company who gave their time and effort to the creation of this book, especially Lynn Messina, Sandra Watson, Gray Young, Norris Smith, Rich Stein, Jennifer Peloso, and Clifford Thompson. Many thanks also to Karen Duda, Peter Herman, Christopher Mari, and Geoffrey Orens for their advice and assistance. Lastly, a very special thanks must go to Richard Marcinko, whose invaluable contributions to this book are very much appreciated.

Jeremy K. Brown
June 2003

I. Theaters of Modern War

Editor's Introduction

U ntil the early days of the 20th century, war was fought primarily on the battlefield, with regiments of soldiers marching on each other or firing over fence lines or from foxholes. World War I, the first truly modern war, expanded the battlefield to include the seas and skies. In World War II, as Allied forces made their way through Europe, the conflict ushered in a new age of urban warfare. In Korea and Vietnam, American troops fought in canopy jungle, rice paddies, and underground tunnels against a largely unseen enemy. Today, the battlefields are limitless. Troops fighting in the Middle East must be ready for searing heat, sandstorms, and a 40-degree difference in temperature between day and night. On the high seas, Littoral Combat Ships may soon plow the waters, their radar-absorbing hulls making them nearly undetectable. Meanwhile, space-based weapons might one day orbit the Earth, seeking out targets with unmatched precision. Section I of this book covers the theaters of modern warfare and the battles that may be fought there.

Many people in the world, particularly in America, cannot conceive of a heated battle being fought in the streets of their cities. Nevertheless, September 11th showed that the battles of the 21st century can, and most likely will, be fought anywhere. Ron Martz's article "U.S. Soldiers Train for Urban Warfare" shows what American forces are doing to prepare for city-based fighting. Martz outlines the intense training they undergo and explains how soldiers are more likely to die in house-to-house fighting than they are on a more open field. Martz shows how an army's ability to fight effectively can be compromised by an urban environment, given the limited maneuverability of tanks and the manner in which helicopters can be transformed from powerful fighting machines to targets of opportunity.

Since the Gulf War in 1991, and with tensions continuing to boil in the Middle East, much attention has been paid to desert fighting. Tim Ripley provides a close examination of desert combat in his article "Fighting in Sand Land." He explains how military strategists must rethink their approach to fighting in this new environment, as evidenced by the fact that, in such an expansive setting, an army has almost no place to hide. Ripley also discusses the role of global positioning systems (GPS), which allow soldiers to maintain their bearings even in sandstorms or at night. Another factor troops in the desert must consider is air-conditioning. A luxury to the average person, with temperatures reaching 40 to 50 degrees Celsius in most deserts, it is a necessity to soldiers. Everything from vehicles to satellite transmitters to shelters must have their temperatures regulated if they are to function properly.

Fighting on the ocean is nothing new, but Otis Port and Stan Crock discuss the next step in naval warfare in their article "Guerrilla Ships for a New Kind of War." The threat of shallow-water attacks by smaller boats, as occurred with the USS *Cole* in 2000, has prompted the Navy to begin envisioning quicker boats with better stealth capabilities. These ships will also be better armed to provide support to troops fighting on land. The authors predict the end of the somewhat romanticized era of big ships fighting on the high seas and instead see these crafts as an integral part of a wide-ranging land, air, and sea assault.

Space-based combat is becoming more of a reality than simply Saturday-matinee fare for *Star Wars* fans. While the Luke Skywalkers of the world may have to wait to strap themselves into an X-wing fighter to save the galaxy, orbital weapons platforms capable of pinpointing specific targets are already being developed. In recent years, this has become something of a hot-button issue. In his article "Space Weapons: Refuting the Critics," Steven Lambakis examines the debate over space-based weaponry from both angles. He references the Outer Space Treaty of 1967, which forbids the deployment of nuclear weapons in space, and shows the loopholes through which various countries can slip other weapons. He also outlines the possibility of international tensions rising in the wake of the use of such weaponry. In addition, he argues that weaponizing space could provide a quick, decisive end to various conflicts and ultimately ensure lasting peace.

Perhaps the battlefield that best defines 21st-century warfare is the one in cyberspace. Terrorists could conceivably disable power and water supplies and inhibit rescue efforts, all via computers. Bruce Berkowitz's article "Information Warfare: Time to Prepare" delves into the problem, examining the challenges defense planners face, the techniques information terrorists might employ, and the infrastructures that are the most vulnerable to this kind of warfare.

U.S. Soldiers Train for Urban Warfare[1]

By Ron Martz
The Atlanta Journal-Constitution, November 16, 2002

The young Army infantry recruits were just a few weeks shy of graduation when they received their baptism into the chaos that is urban warfare.

In a makeshift village on the eastern side of this sprawling base, they learned to peer around the corners of buildings without presenting an inviting target.

They learned how to cross streets in four-man teams while protecting one another.

They learned how to crash into rooms that could be occupied by enemy soldiers.

And they learned repeatedly that it is far easier to die in house-to-house fighting than it is to survive.

"This is the bloodiest, worst fighting we do. You can be perfect at it, and a lot of you are still going to die," Sgt. Zachary Pritchard, an instructor in urban warfare, tells hushed recruits.

As America's military ramps up for a possible attack on Iraq, it must prepare for the possibility that Saddam Hussein's troops will try to lure Americans into the nightmare that is urban warfare.

During the Persian Gulf War, the Iraqis were devastated when they tried to go toe-to-toe in the open desert against superior American technology and training. Iraqi officials have hinted they might try to blunt the U.S. advantage by retreating to the cities.

Whether they are bluffing remains to be seen, but American military officials know urban combat is a great equalizer. Some liken it to "a knife fight in a phone booth."

But that does not seem to worry the recruits at Fort Benning during this urban-combat training session.

"It's an eye-opener, but I love it," said Pvt. Brian Floyd, 18, of Los Angeles. "This is what I signed up for, kicking in doors and jumping through windows."

The Worst Policy

More than 2,500 years ago, the Chinese philosopher and military strategist Sun Tzu wrote: "The worst policy is to attack cities." Military strategists know that still holds true. The problems of urban warfare are many, the solutions few.

Helicopters are more vulnerable in cities, as Americans learned during the battle of Mogadishu in 1993.

Communications are often spotty, making it difficult for commanders to keep track of their troops.

Tanks and other armored vehicles have difficulty maneuvering and are easy targets. The Russians learned that with deadly consequences in their efforts to oust Chechen rebels from the city of Grozny.

Long-range precision weapons such as Tomahawk cruise missiles and smart bombs are of limited use.

And the defenders of a city know the battlefield far better than the invading troops, making it easier for them to inflict heavy casualties. They can fight building-to-building and room-to-room using familiar rooftops, rubble and sewers to slow attacking troops.

"All cities present a significant problem when conducting urban operations," said retired Marine Lt. Gen. Bernard Trainor.

Fighting in Baghdad could be even worse than in other cities, added Trainor, a defense analyst with the Council on Foreign Relations, who spent time in the Iraqi capital during the Iran-Iraq war.

Baghdad is like two cities in one, split by the Tigris River. The west side is modern and symmetrical, so gathering intelligence about it would be relatively easy, Trainor said. The east side, though, is a mixture of new and centuries-old structures—"a warren of interconnected streets and alleyways without any pattern."

10th Mountain Division—Operation Enduring Freedom (Source: www.militaryphotos.net*).*

"It's really more difficult than Mogadishu," the general said. "Where the fighting took place in Mogadishu was fairly coherent and structurally symmetrical."

During the battle of Mogadishu, 18 Army Rangers were killed by Somali gunmen and dozens more were wounded. More than 1,000 Somalis are believed to have died.

Military analysts say Saddam has positioned about 100,000 Special Republican Guard troops around Baghdad for the city's defense. But there are questions about how hard any of them will fight. During the last gulf war, Iraqi troops ran or surrendered by the thousands.

Troops at the Bull's-eye

Retired Army Col. Danny McKnight does not believe what happened in Mogadishu says much about what might happen in Baghdad.

McKnight was commander of the ground convoy sent into Mogadishu to take out some of the top lieutenants of Somali warlord Mohammed Farah Aidid. They had been captured by Delta Force soldiers and were being taken by McKnight's Rangers for question-

---

"Everybody had a weapon. You were fighting everybody you saw. You were fighting 360 degrees."—**Ret. Army Col. Danny McKnight**

---

ing. Then a U.S. helicopter was shot down, and McKnight's group tried to rescue those in the downed chopper.

At that point the city seemed to explode.

The battle of Mogadishu began with what essentially was a raid to take prisoners, McKnight said. If the United States sends troops into Baghdad, it will be with a larger force and more planning will go into the operation.

"It is going to have to be a well-conceived, well-planned and well-organized attack. And it will have to be focused on particular objectives," said McKnight, now director of homeland security for Brevard County in Florida.

It is also unlikely that the population of Baghdad will join in the fight, as did the Somalis in Mogadishu, he said.

"I think what was the unexpected piece in that fight was that everybody had a weapon. You were fighting everybody you saw. You were fighting 360 degrees. We weren't fighting an organized fight against another organized unit," said McKnight.

McKnight said the casualty rate among the Rangers could have been "five to six times higher than it was" had the unit not trained repeatedly in urban combat tactics and techniques.

"A Ranger battalion without question was the most well-trained unit in the Army at that time, with the possible exception of the Delta guys," said McKnight.

Simulations and Losses

Training for urban combat has not always been an Army priority, said Capt. Brent Cummings, an instructor in urban warfare at Fort Benning. The last time American forces were involved in sustained urban combat was nearly 35 years ago, in the battle for Hue in Vietnam.

"In the Cold War we trained to fight the Soviet Union on the plains of Europe. Our doctrine was to avoid the urban environment. Today we know we're going to have to fight in an urban environment," said Cummings, who teaches captains who are about to become infantry company commanders.

Cummings has been instrumental in the design of a computer simulation that he says will teach "the basic blocking and tackling of urban warfare."

With a development price tag of just under $2 million, the game will try to replicate what happens, or what is supposed to happen, when troops do or don't do certain things in urban combat.

The simulation is scheduled to be unveiled Jan. 1, and if it gets the Army's go-ahead after an 18-week test, Cummings said everybody in the Army could have a copy.

The simulation "will train these soldiers to be better leaders and ultimately will save guys' lives," he said.

Still, said Cummings, "there is no substitute for muddy-boots training."

Army infantry recruits get only a brief introduction to urban warfare, a two-day crash course. They get more after they graduate and get to their units. Virtually every major military base now has its own mock village, known as a Military Operations in Urban Terrain, or MOUT, site.

Fort Benning has two such sites: a rudimentary village known as Malone MOUT where recruits train, and a more sophisticated town with concrete and steel buildings and a sewer system, the McKenna MOUT site.

In recent weeks the pace of training has picked up. About 1,000 troops from the Army's 10th Mountain Division recently went through a three-week training rotation in urban combat at Fort Polk, La. Marines have been training in mock cities on Guam and in Southern California.

Even the best-trained troops can expect to suffer 30 percent casualties or higher, according to Army doctrine.

To avoid such carnage in an Iraq attack, Trainor says, the United States would probably try to isolate major cities and target their key sites, rather than fight block by block.

Still, the general said, any fighting in cities "is a tough proposition, and casualties are usually high."

Fighting in Sand Land[2]

BY TIM RIPLEY
ARMADA INTERNATIONAL, DECEMBER 2002/JANUARY 2003

Desert Warfare 2003

Deserts by their very nature are mostly desolate, uncultivated, barren and uninhabited regions. Huge sections of the Middle East, Central Asia, North and Southern Africa, the Americas and Australia are termed desert. They share many common characteristics, such as lack of or minimal vegetation and water sources, but specific climates and terrain features can vary greatly from one region to another.

The need for armies to move across deserts as a self-contained force throws up many unique equipment requirements. Every vehicle sent into the desert must have the same level of mobility, for an army is only as mobile as its slowest vehicle. A key element of desert mobility is ensuring that all the logistic equipment and resources can be moved across country by vehicle, most importantly because enemy flanking moves could threaten logistic supply lines.

The campaigns in North Africa between 1941 and 1943 were the first time large mechanised forces clashed in desert terrain and the lessons of this conflict heavily influenced post-war desert warfare tactics. As a result, new methods of maintaining mobility across sandy desert terrain, vehicle maintenance and logistic support protocols in regions with no road or rail infrastructure were developed.

The Arab-Israeli war and other conflicts in the Middle East since the 1940s have provided new lessons and experiences as new weapons and technologies have entered service. American, British, French and other allied forces have learned a great deal from their participation in the 1991 war against Iraq. These lessons have been put to use over the past decade in a series of major exercises and operations in the Middle East, as well as during operations in southwest Afghanistan during Operation Enduring Freedom in late 2001.

These campaigns certainly brought to light the problems encountered when operating "smart" weapons based on computer technology in hot and dusty climates, but also underscored the potential of satellite navigation systems. Locating targets in desert terrain as well as concealing troops and equipment from high-technology sensors have also emerged as major issues.

---

2. Reprinted with permission of Armada International, Zurich, Switzerland, *www.armada.ch.*

Some of the problems of operating a modern high technology army in extreme desert conditions were highlighted during the British Saif Sareea II exercise in Oman in 2001. This saw some 22,500 personnel, 6500 vehicles, 49 fixed-wing aircraft and 44 helicopters deploying to the country to test Britain's rapid reaction capability and strengthen links with the Omani military. The British National Audit Office (NAO) reported that Vickers Defence Systems Challenger 2 tanks without desert warfare modifications suffered from 30 per cent unavailability rates. British helicopters were badly affected by the climate with an average availability rate of 55 per cent during the exercise. The BAE Systems AS-90 self-propelled gun, also badly affected by the heat, could only be moved at night, according to the NAO. Tents, communication systems, cargo handling equipment and logistic vehicles were all found to have reacted poorly to the desert conditions.

An enduring feature of desert warfare tactics is the emphasis on strategic operation and tactical mobility.

An enduring feature of desert warfare tactics is the emphasis on strategic operation and tactical mobility to ensure battlefield success. Desert battlefields cover huge areas, making it almost impossible for fixed defenses or terrain features to block enemy movement. While the desert can be a challenging environment, an army that retains the ability to manoeuver has the potential to strike at will at an opponent's open flank or concentrate on an enemy's weak spot.

Navigation

The featureless nature of most deserts and problems associated with shifting sand have always plagued armed forces operating in desert regions. Magnetic and sun compasses were the staple of desert navigation until the final decade of the 20th century, but they had severe limitations and required a high level of skill and experience. In addition, these traditional methods of navigation are not accurate enough to allow the use of modern precision guided munitions, as the latter need precise location information to allow targeting data to be injected into them.

The advent of cheap and light satellite navigation technology, based on the US Global Positioning Satellite (GPS) system, has transformed desert warfare. During Operation Desert Storm, tens of thousands of hand-held GPS navigation devices were made available to coalition soldiers. Many were made by Magellan and were soon popularly known as "sluggers."

These devices allowed large formations of coalition troops to move across country in bad weather and at night, giving users accurate positioning data to within a few metres. Previously, troops would have had to halt in such conditions until a method of navigation became possible. GPS also allowed coalition artillery and air power to be used in close proximity to friendly forces with greater confidence.

Nightstalker MH-47E Crew Over Afghanistan—Operation Enduring Freedom.

The 1991 Gulf war also saw the combat debut of embedded GPS in vehicles and weapon systems, such as the Lockheed Martin/ Loral Multiple Launch Rocket Systems (MLRS). Over the past eleven years these systems have become commonplace in a wide span of vehicles, such as main battle tanks and even light utility vehicles.

Selective availability of GPS data was phased out as a result of the 1996 executive order by President Bill Clinton, so non-US military users and civilians can now achieve 10 to 15-metre accuracy, compared to the previously available 100 metres. The size of handheld devices has been considerably reduced over the past decade, with mobile-phone-sized GPS devices now available. Most can also be easily integrated into laptop computers and other communication devices.

GPS receiver technology is now widely available to military and civil markets. In July 2001, the French-owned Thales Group acquired US GPS market leader Magellan and merged it with Thales Navigation. The four leading brands represented in this new GPS company include MLR, DSNP, Magellan and Ashtech. Thales Navigation streamlined the brands represented to maximize marketing and communications efforts. Magellan became the company's consumer GPS brand worldwide and Ashtech became the company's professional mark. Other GPS manufacturers include CMC Electronics, Trimble, Garmin, CSI, Novatel, Rojone, GPSoft, Fugawi and Micropulse.

There are many companies around the world that package GPS into vehicle navigation systems, including KVH and Smiths Aerospace in America and Litef in Germany.

Mobility

High levels of cross-country mobility are essential for all vehicles involved in desert warfare. Four-by-four (4 x 4) capability is a minimum and larger vehicles should, if possible, be powered on all axles.

Winches and tow cables or bars need to be issued on a wide scale so vehicles bogged in soft sand or stuck in wadis (depressions) can be quickly recovered. Matting is also essential to place under wheels of vehicles being pulled out of soft sand to facilitate rescue.

There are numerous manufacturers of highly capable cross-country military vehicles including Switzerland's Bucher-Guyer, the manufacturer and supplier of the Duro family of 4 x 4 and 6 x 6 transports for on- and off-road military applications. In Germany Daimler Chrysler produces the Mercedes-Benz Military Vehicles brand. Italy's Iveco makes tactical trucks and military utility vehicles. In Finland Sisu makes a wide range of high mobility tactical vehicles, as does Tatra in the Czech Republic and Acmat in France.

In America, AM General's High Mobility Multipurpose Wheeled Vehicle (Humvee or Hummer) has become the standard utility vehicle of the US Army for use in desert regions.

In production since 1982, the Oshkosh Truck Corporation's Hemett (Heavy Mobility Expanded Tactical Truck) is the backbone of US Army logistics. Hemetts saw extensive action during Desert Shield/Storm and received rave reviews. Over 15,000 have been built for US and foreign armed forces. Today, Oshkosh is in the process of re-manufacturing older vehicles as well as producing new builds. This refurbishment updates the trucks with the latest technology at less than 60 percent of the cost of a new vehicle.

The eight-wheel-drive M1070 Het (Heavy Equipment Transporter) built by Oshkosh for the US Army brings increased payload and mobility to the military's heavy equipment transport mission. Its primary use is the rapid transport of the 70-plus-ton M1A1 tank to the battlefront. It also transports other tanks, fighting and recovery vehicles, self-propelled howitzers and construction equipment. Oshkosh Truck has built nearly 2000 for the US Army and other customers since August 1992.

Stewart & Stevenson has been the exclusive supplier of the Family of Medium Tactical Vehicles (FMTV) to the US Army since 1991; this includes trucks and companion trailers for on- and off-road use.

Cooling Vehicles and Shelters

The requirement for effective air conditioning in desert conditions is obvious, with temperatures regularly reaching 45 to 50 degrees Celsius in some deserts at the height of summer.

Air conditioning, however, is not just a "nice-to-have-item." It has become mission-critical to cool vital computers and electronic equipment. Where these are mounted in vehicles or metal/composite portable shelters, air conditioning units can be installed easily and run off an integral power supply or be connected to generators. Thermal shielding also needs to be incorporated into the shelter's structure to reduce the power required to cool it effectively. Tents and simple shelters, however, and for obvious reasons, require their own portable air conditioning units.

Satellite dishes and other antennas that need to be placed in the open require the services of portable air conditioning units to pipe cold air around their vital components. Sheets of thermal shielding can be used to wrap around vulnerable areas.

Nevertheless, and this is often forgotten, effective heating is also a must in vehicles and shelters used in desert conditions because the dramatic temperature drops that can occur at night in the desert can be equally as problematic as high daytime temperatures.

The need to operate air conditioning and heating systems at an intensive rate can result in significant increases in fuel consumption by vehicles and generators, requiring extra resources to be made available for the transport and delivery of this fuel.

Most shelters and tents customised for desert warfare are packaged together by specialist companies, such as ACD Air Shelter and ACMH Sameto in France, Fokker Special Products in the Netherlands, Dornier in Germany, Gichner Shelter Systems and the Mesa Corporation in the United States. The British company Insys, formerly Hunting, is in partnership with Giat under the Euro-Shelter banner to design and manufacture mobile shelters, medical and logistic systems.

US Bunkers of Miami, Florida, manufactures efficient shelters that resemble space vehicles and can be airlifted or sling loaded to any location and easily positioned to begin work immediately. The shelters come with any combination of options, including an emergency escape hatch and ladder, exterior video cameras, radar, communication and surveillance system equipment and M-2 guns above and below. The shelter doors can be plain, bullet-or heatproof, and manually, electrically, hydraulically or mechanically operated, and the shelter can include air conditioning, heating, an internal water supply tank, a fuel tank or even solar panels with a battery pack.

The specialist air conditioning equipment needed for desert warfare is available from companies like Behr of Germany, which specializes in exchange systems, cooling and air conditioning equipment for engines, transmissions, crew compartments and electronics. For the Leopard 2, Behr supplied radiators, charge-air coolers, transmission oil coolers, fuel coolers and oil coolers for the turret hydraulics, water-to-water heat exchangers, engine oil heat exchangers and heaters. Further vehicles equipped with Behr cooling systems include the Pandur, Piranha, Ariete, Pizarro, Fuchs, Wiesel, Leclerc, Rokit, Centauro, Ulan, BMR, GTK, KI Howitzer Korea, Flying Tiger and the PzH 2000.

Dantherm of Denmark has developed portable warm air heaters and transportable air conditioning units for use in the most extreme conditions. Hunter Manufacturing designs tent, shelter, cargo and vehicle heating systems that can include NBC filters and positive pressure systems.

Dust

Sand and dust in desert regions can wreak havoc with the smooth operation of weapon systems, engines and other machinery. There are several ways to minimize and overcome this problem. A major issue is the ingestion of dust into engines, causing damage and ulti- mately causing power failure. Tracked vehicles in particular are prone to dust problems because their tracks throw up huge clouds of dust. Given enough dust, engine air intake filters can clog up to the extent of totally starving the engine, which will eventually stall.

Sand and dust in desert regions can wreak havoc with the smooth operation of weapon systems, engines and other machinery.

Side skirts that force dust down can help minimize the problem but the air intake filter is the item that needs to be concentrated on. Desert filters need to be significantly more effective than those designed for temperate climates. The air filtration systems needed for desert warfare are usually designed and manufactured by the original equipment manufacturer of the armoured vehicles con- cerned. Vickers Defense Systems, for example developed a "deserti- sation" kit for the Challenger 2s it sold to Oman and had offered elements of this package to the British.

Because they suck up such enormous volumes of air compared with diesels, and thereby a similarly increased proportion of impuri- ties, the Textron Lycoming gas turbines of the General Dynamics M1A1 Abrams tanks used by the US, Egyptian and Saudi armies are standard fitted with sand filtration kits equipped with special self-cleaning devices because of their need to operate almost exclu- sively in desert conditions in the Middle East or on desert training areas in the continental United States.

Small arms, machine guns, tank main armament and artillery can also be severely affected by dust. Special lubricants can be used to prevent dust clogging but ultimately the only way to solve this prob- lem is by regular and effective maintenance.

Helicopters are particularly vulnerable to dust during desert oper- ations. Flying through dust clouds at low level can cause engine fail- ure if filters do not properly protect them. Companies such as Pall produce solutions to this problem, which employ particle separation technology to filter sand and grit without reducing the airflow in a helicopter's engine and thus not affecting its power output. Rotor blades can also be severely damaged by dust erosion on their leading edges, which in effect is similar to the application of high pressure sand blasting. Many modern blades have reinforced leading edges but older blades often do not. One way to protect these blades is by the application of adhesive strips of Teflon-based material. This has a limited effect because the tape only has a short life until it flakes off. Landing aids, such as radar altimeters, can also be quite useful when pilots can become disorientated in dust clouds generated by their helicopter. The phenomenon is known as "brown out."

Optically-guided weapons on aircraft and helicopters flying at low level over desert regions are also worthy of attention. The standard glass or Perspex coverings of the optical sensors or seeker heads on missiles or bomb guidance units can be badly scratched and scarred by high speed dust impacts, which can severely affect the accuracy of these weapons. QinetiQ in Britain has developed a diamond dome to cover precision-guided weapons in cooperation with De Beers Industrial Diamonds.

The domes are made using a CVD (Chemical Vapour Deposition) technique, which is a meta-stable process, where diamond is formed from excited carbon atoms in a gaseous state, at temperatures and pressures at which graphite is thermodynamically more stable. Under the correct conditions, diamond crystals thousandths of a millimetre in diameter form on a substrate and evolve into a continuous sheet of polycrystalline diamond. After growth the domes have to be configured into optical components, accurately processing the inner and outer faces to be parallel with highly polished surfaces. The finished components exhibit low loss, negligible scatter at infrared wavelengths and are suitable for a wide range of imaging applications.

Water Supply

To survive and fight in hot desert conditions, soldiers require significant quantities of water over and above normal requirements in temperate zones. For personnel working in headquarters, rear areas or driving soft skinned vehicles, normal bottled water is usually sufficient. Frontline infantry soldiers and armoured fighting vehicles crews, however, need specialized water-carrying equipment that enables them to drink without interrupting their combat activity.

CamelBak has developed an extensive range of water-carrying products that are easily and comfortably attached to web equipment or rucksacks and allow the wearer to drink through a mouthpiece without needing to stop and pull out a water bottle from a holder. Similar products are also available for vehicle crews.

Following suit, Blackhawk Industries offers the Hydrastorm line of hydration systems. A Hydrastorm system contains a Nytaneon nylon reservoir for extra strength, as well as secure on-off and a triangle shaped delta bite valve. IVS back panels and compression moulded closed cell foam with channels provide performance and stability.

Uniforms

High temperatures and dusty conditions obviously bring with them specialized uniform requirements. Cotton and other natural fibres provide the best material for desert uniforms, reducing sweating and discomfort.

Thick leather boots can be extremely uncomfortable in hot climates and plastic soles have also been known to melt in high temperatures. Lightweight leather or canvas boots with good ventilation are essential to reduce sweating, which can be very uncomfortable and lead to foot injuries and blisters.

Nuclear, chemical and biological (NBC) protective suits in desert conditions, not surprisingly, can cause severe problems for the

---

Hiding an army in the desert is not an easy task because of the lack of buildings.

---

wearer. Wearing a traditional activated-carbon-loaded filter-layered NBC suit over a normal uniform can result in the wearer sweating profusely and ultimately lead to dehydration if water consumption is not increased significantly.

In an attempt to reduce the dehydration effects of wearing NBC protective clothing in hot climates the German firm BIOcher has produced the Saratoga multi-role uniform that provides NBC protection. These use material with adsorptive filter layers and have been purchased in large quantities by the US military and 18 other nations around the world, including several Middle Eastern countries.

Camouflage

Hiding an army in the desert is not an easy task because of the lack of buildings, forests and hills that are usually used to aid concealment in temperate or tropical zones.

Until the advent of ground surveillance radar and thermal imaging sensors, desert camouflage involved following relatively straightforward principles. There was first a need to blend into the colour of the desert; to this end vehicles would be painted in sand-yellow colours and camouflage nets used to disguise the shape of vehicles. Secondly, trenches and sand ramparts called berms would be dug to hide men and vehicles below ground to break up their shape and make it more difficult for them to be spotted at long ranges. Earth excavators, bulldozers and detachable dozer blades for tracked armoured vehicles allowed armies to quickly disappear below ground level in desert terrain. The use of explosives was sometimes necessary in rocky regions to blast open the ground for excavation.

Modern sensor technology, however, has forced the development of new camouflage technology to provide protection throughout the electromagnetic spectrum, from visual through to near infrared, thermal and radar spectrums. Camouflage nets used in desert warfare now need to be backed by heat reflective material to "merge" the temperature of the vehicle being protected with the surrounding ambient temperature. To combat synthetic aperture radar used by ground surveillance aircraft, radar defeating material has to be incorporated in camouflage netting packages. This scatters incoming signals, reflecting them in many different angular directions and reducing the reflected image received by the enemy radar processor. The shape of the netting can also be tailored to maximize its "stealth" qualities.

SSZ in Switzerland, Fibrotex in America, Blaschke Wehrtechnik in Austria and J & S Franklin in Britain all produce camouflage netting products to meet desert warfare requirements. Although some of the above companies tackle the spectrum analysis issue, there is little doubt that the most popular firm in this respect is Saab Barracuda. This Swedish company has been tricking heat, electromagnetic waves and naked eye perceptions for years now and has been the suppliers of the multiple spectrum camouflage suite used by the United Arab Emirate's Leclerc tanks.

Sensors

The advent of thermal imaging technology has transformed desert warfare and has become the de facto surveillance and targeting system used by land forces deployed to desert regions.

The ability to locate heat and differentiate it from the natural heat of the ground at long ranges has, to a significant degree, negated the protection previously provided by cover and camouflage. Superior thermal sights used by the coalition forces during the 1991 Gulf war proved decisive, allowing them to engage Iraqi troops at long ranges and often before Baghdad's forces had spotted the coalition troops.

Thermal sight technology has since advanced considerably to the extent that even infantry squads now have some thermal imaging capability. When combined with lightweight ground surveillance radars, thermal imaging systems make it almost impossible for an opponent to use the night or bad weather as a shield. In flat desert terrain these systems take on added significance and utility. Major players in the thermal imaging market include Thales and BAE Systems in Europe, TIT, DRS and Raytheon in the United States.

Thales is also a leading supplier of portable ground surveillance radars. Its Squire system is a small radar for the detection of moving ground targets up to a range of 24 km. The system, consisting of two major elements each weighing less than 17 kilograms, is compact, lightweight and can be set up in minutes.

The fielding of millimetric wave radars, such as the Lockheed Martin Longbow installed on the Boeing AH64D Apache, offers the prospect of further revolutionising desert warfare. With their ability to "see through" bad weather and night and produce 3-D images of targets, millimetre wave radars will give those who have them an unprecedented view of the desert battlefield, stripping away what little cover exists. Current generation camouflage netting will soon be made obsolete, requiring new solutions to defeat the disadvantage this technology provides. Vehicles, however, will continue to remain highly vulnerable unless protected with "active" defensive systems, such as jammers.

Desert Future

Fighting in the desert has always been a challenge. The age-old battle with the climate and terrain continues but the introduction of modern weapon systems has meant the desert warrior of the 21st century has a far more difficult task. Modern surveillance technology makes it almost impossible to hide on the desert battlefield.

Technology offers some solutions to these problems, but without regular training and hands-on familiarisation soldiers operating in desert conditions will always be at a disadvantage. Time and again it has been proven that armies venturing into deserts without proper preparation and planning do so at their own risk.

Guerrilla Ships for a New Kind of War[3]

By Otis Port and Stan Crock
Business Week, January 27, 2003

Last summer, in the Pentagon's biggest war game ever, an invasion fleet heading for a fictional Middle East nation got soundly trounced in the Persian Gulf. The mighty U.S. Navy was no match for the wily Saddam-like dictator, played by retired Marine Lieutenant General Paul Van Riper. He ruthlessly sent swarms of explosives-laden pleasure boats and old propeller planes on suicide attacks. Together with a few outmoded Silkworm antiship missiles from China, the small boats and planes sank 16 U.S. ships—including the fleet's aircraft carrier and other vessels carrying thousands of marines.

The Navy brass have long been leery of the threat posed to its big ships by antiship missiles and by swarms of little boats in "brown water," meaning close to shore. Years before the suicide-boat attack on the destroyer USS Cole in October, 2000, some Navy officials wanted to develop smaller, faster war boats for brown-water battles. Dubbed Streetfighter, the concept was championed by Vice-Admiral Arthur K. Cebrowski, who now heads the Pentagon's new Office of Force Transformation.

The idea ran into widespread opposition, however. Critics fretted that the little ships would suffer high casualties, which might make the Navy less attractive to new volunteers and undermine congressional support. Novelty was also a liability. For more than a century, the U.S. Navy has been geared to fight on the high seas. And in those deep, blue waters, bigger is better. "Zipping around in souped-up speedboats is not what the Navy has done," says military analyst John E. Pike, head of GlobalSecurity.org in Alexandria, Va.

Streetfighter advocates countered that the U.S. lost its last blue-water rival a decade ago with the collapse of the Soviet Union. Today, many naval officers doubt there will ever be another deep-ocean slugfest like those in World War II. The Navy's main task now is supporting ground forces and peacekeeping missions—which means getting close to shore because naval guns currently have a range of only 13 miles. In such brown water, big ships are sitting ducks: In less than a minute, an antiship missile can whiz from land and smack a ship several miles at sea.

The advocates won. And the Navy may soon get its first Street-fighter—called a Littoral Combat Ship (LCS). Six contractor teams recently submitted LCS design concepts to the Pentagon, and next month, the Defense Dept. will pick three designs for further refine-ment. The ultimate winner could go into production as soon as 2005. Defense Secre-tary Donald H. Rumsfeld, also a proponent, and Cebrowski have pointed out that LCS could allow a significant expansion of today's 315-ship Navy without substantially raising costs. They want to buy 50 to 70 of the new war ships at less than $220 million a pop. That's about a quarter of the price tag for a new destroyer. And some of the new designs might be cheaper.

They want to buy 50 to 70 of the new war ships at less than $220 million a pop.

The LCS concepts are believed to range in length from about half the size of a 500-foot destroyer down to the 80-foot size of the PT boats of World War II. But they won't look like anything in today's fleet. Above its deck, the mini-destroyer proposed by Northrop Grumman Corp.'s team resembles an F-117 stealth bomber—and below deck is a durable composite-plastics hull. It's modeled on the Visby-class 270-ft. ships that Sweden's Kockums is building for the Swedish Navy. How important will stealth be in brown water? "We're trying to determine that right now," says Admiral Donald P. Loren, the Navy's deputy director for surface ships. With a vessel that can plow through the waves at 50 knots (55 mph) or more, he says, perhaps some of the extra cost of slanted, radar-absorbing panels can be traded for more ships.

Other proposals are equally unconventional. The team led by Gen-eral Dynamics Corp.'s Bath Iron Works envisions a trimaran hull adapted from a high-speed ferry being built in Australia by Austal Ltd. And Lockheed Martin Corp.'s group probably offered a catama-ran patterned after its 105-ft. prototype Sea Slice vessel and a big-ger, 310-ft. cargo ferry built by Australia's International Catamarans (Incat) Tasmania. The Navy is "being challenged to think differently," said Chief of Naval Operations Admiral Vernon E. Clark at a naval-warfare symposium last October. "It is a differ-ent time."

New computer technology is helping to win over some former oppo-nents. The Navy began developing a computerized combat network more than a decade ago, aiming for the integration of military sen-sors, which proved so effective in Afghanistan. Its Cooperative Engagement Capability (CEC) system, built by Raytheon Co., is already deployed on more than 20 big ships. So, when Streetfighters take to the waves, CEC could help them outfox opponents. Their skippers would get real-time intelligence gathered by radar on big ships farther out to sea, by video cameras and other sensors on manned and unmanned aircraft overhead, and by robot submarines and speedboats—also under development—that will go in harm's way without endangering sailors.

Analyst Pike says he's fascinated by the whole issue of revamping the Navy for near-shore duty. "But the fundamental question," he adds, is whether the Navy can scuttle "its big-ship mind-set." If it does, Streetfighters might provide a brown-water punch that could prevent real-world disasters such as the Navy's make-believe one last summer.

Space Weapons: Refuting the Critics[4]

BY STEVEN LAMBAKIS
POLICY REVIEW, FEBRUARY & MARCH 2001

Clashes over the military use of space, usually a result of proposals to fund politically controversial weapons programs, have agitated and unsettled the country at various times throughout the space age. But though the world has changed, the intellectual and doctrinal foundations underlying the debate have not.

Since 1967, the Outer Space Treaty has banned the deployment of nuclear weapons in space. But what about other weapons? Although the United States has no plans to do so, it could deploy antisatellite (ASAT) or space-based ballistic missile defense (BMD) interceptors using conventional explosives or high velocity impact. Currently, the Pentagon has technology development programs for the Kinetic Energy ASAT and the Space-Based Laser. In the long term, satellites or space planes could be designed to exploit high-energy laser, electromagnetic pulse, or high-power microwave technologies to degrade targets in space or on earth. President Reagan's Strategic Defense Initiative explored the feasibility of many such weapons systems. To some, these new-era tools of war hold out special military promise; to others, they represent a security and foreign relations nightmare.

Political excitement over the use of space also ripples through the foreign policy arena. Prompted by U.S. discussions and war games featuring space control and BMD weapons, in February 2000 the Chinese delegation to the United Nations Conference on Disarmament circulated a paper identifying "a present and pressing necessity" to prevent an arms race in outer space. A treaty forestalling the "weaponization" of space, argued the delegation, would have "the greatest bearing on global peace and security."

Moscow agrees with Beijing on this subject. Russian officials regard the 1972 U.S.-Soviet Anti-Ballistic Missile (ABM) treaty, which prohibits nationwide defenses against intercontinental ballistic missiles, as a bulwark against ideas for basing BMD interceptors and other conventional weapons in orbit. Russian President Vladimir Putin offered to host an international conference in 2001 to explore ways to prevent the "militarization" of outer space and enhance the current regime of international space law.

---

4. Article by Steven Lambakis from *Policy Review*, February and March 2001. Copyright © *Policy Review*. Reprinted with permission.

Historically, America's vision has been that space should be free for transit and exploitation by all governments and private entities, provided such activities pose no harm to U.S. interests or security. Questions surrounding, first, the enforcement of this vision and, second, the possible use of space to strengthen America's military prowess naturally will arise as the country struggles to resolve a more radical uncertainty: For purposes of national defense, should space be treated like the land, sea, and air? Or is there something different and sacrosanct about this forbidding environment?

Despite marked physical differences among the earthly and orbital environments, in my view there really are no meaningful characteristics that allow us to consider them differently from the point of view of policy and strategy. The ability to leverage outer space will continue to grow in importance for modern military forces and may make possible even more effective forms of combat.

Yet there are those who reach the opposite conclusion concerning the potential impact of space weapons on national security and international peace. They have argued their case in learned journals, the popular press, and before congressional committees—in many cases, repeating arguments first made decades ago. It is past time for a thorough review of the case for halting the progress of weapons at the edge of earth's atmosphere.

For purposes of national defense, should space be treated like the land, sea, and air?

Stability Then and Now

The case for treating space as a sanctuary is grounded in two central concerns. The first is that the introduction of space weapons would radically destabilize security relationships. The second is that arming the heavens would undermine U.S. foreign policy by unnecessarily torturing relationships with allies (and potential warfighting partners)—and would cause anti-American coalitions to form and wage political and economic warfare against U.S. interests abroad.

The case against combat activities in space draws heavily on 1950s-vintage theories of strategic stability that evolved to support U.S. policy on nuclear weapons. As policy makers gave up on early disarmament initiatives on practical grounds, many who pondered defense schemes in a world with nuclear weapons focused on arms control and theories about the stability of deterrence. Responsible leaders sought political solutions and the establishment of international legal mechanisms for methodically reducing nuclear arms and improving transparency and predictability in decision making. This security approach sought to eliminate the possibility that the United States or the Soviet Union would perceive an opportunity for a "first strike" against the other. Such fears of nuclear instability and the escalation of regional conflicts have survived the Cold War and enliven commentary on national security today.

In this view, the military use of space has both stabilizing and destabilizing potential. Satellites perform nonthreatening, largely benign, and stabilizing military functions that contribute to nuclear deterrence and transparency. But weapons in space, especially anti-satellite weapons, would risk impairing the very instruments and sensors we deploy in orbit to monitor potential enemies and maintain reliable communications. Reconnaissance satellites observe arms control compliance and provide strategic warning of an impending crisis. Infrared sensors on early warning satellites detect ballistic missile launches and, together with observation spacecraft, remain central pillars of peace and stability in the international system. A sudden attack against such spacecraft, in this view, would lead at once to heightened alert status and would aggravate instability in command structures. In today's Russia, the situation may be even more dangerous, given the deterioration of command and control capabilities since the fall of the Soviet Union in 1991.

Misperceptions falling out of cloaked activities in space could lead

---

Weapons in space, especially antisatellite weapons, would risk impairing the very instruments and sensors we deploy in orbit to monitor potential enemies.

---

to war and prime a conflict for escalation to higher levels of destruction, in this reasoning. Indeed, one may draw parallels with the famous gunfight at the OK Corral. When the first shot rang out in Tombstone, Ariz., the reflexive response of all was to shoot wildly at anything that moved. Assuming the proliferation of space weapons and a similar instance of provocation, combatants would be tempted to respond in a similar fashion. Each side would have very little time to assess the threat and select an appropriate response.

The deployment of space weapons, in the view of their critics, would accordingly increase sensitivity to vulnerability and needlessly heighten fears and tensions, thereby undermining deterrence. Out of fear of losing everything in a surprise war, a "first strike" against space assets (possibly a prelude to a first nuclear strike) could well make this fear self-fulfilling. In conflict, communications would be hindered, and our decision cycles would slow to the point at which we would not understand the events unfolding in space. The "fog of war" would assume a new density.

In the view of space weapon critics, this is not the only danger. The deployment of spacecraft to gather and channel information of importance to the armed forces has militarized space already; but, they ask, can we not now draw the line to prevent the *weaponization* of space in a dangerous new arms race? After all, U.S. leaders ought not to assume that they can acquire space weapons unchallenged.

Other states would respond. Moreover, those going second (or third or fourth) might have an easier time of it. They would strive to capitalize on years of American research and development, avoiding along the way early mistakes and exorbitant development costs. For prestige, foreign governments will not want to be left behind in this "Revolution in Military Affairs." Indeed, out of self-interest, other states eventually would acquire capabilities to affect the course of war in space and even to strike the United States.

To build weapons for use in space, in this view, would be to recklessly disregard American history—in particularly, U.S. experience with multiple, independently targetable reentry vehicles, or MIRVS. Our attempt to gain a technological edge over the Soviets in the 1970s backfired, critics argue. What resulted was a Soviet campaign to match and eventually surpass the U.S. MIRV capability. When the dust settled, each side had acquired the technology to increase substantially the number of warheads and destroy with alarming efficiency the other's nuclear forces. We might, in this

---

To build weapons for use in space, in this view, would be to recklessly disregard American history.

---

account, expect a similar result after Washington deploys its first space weapon.

Upending Foreign Policy

Finally, critics assert, failure to exercise restraint in space arms would risk upsetting U.S. foreign policy and destabilizing international relationships. The United Nations has provided platforms for denouncing the militarization of space since the late 1950s, when U.S. Ambassador Henry Cabot Lodge expressed the hope before the General Assembly that "future developments in outer space would be devoted exclusively to peaceful and scientific purposes." Over the years, various U.N. state representatives have pleaded with the major powers to take the lead in preserving the purity of this environment.

In this view, deploying arms in environments unexploited by other states would earn for Washington the enmity of capitals around the world. They would see the strongest country in the world trying to become even stronger—and doing so in untraditional, unparalleled ways. This very condition would make it harder to retain friends and allies. The shadow of such weapons would alarm foreign capitals, much as the launch of Sputnik unnerved Washington.

The negative effect of space weapons on foreign opinion could have far-reaching consequences. The multinational coalition assembled by Washington to throw Iraqi forces out of Kuwait in 1991 might not have been possible if the United States had deployed space weapons in disregard of political sensitivities exhibited by the partnership countries. Washington's military plans, moreover, would provoke a costly hostility among potential adversaries and neutral parties in the absence of major threats.

Washington's October 1997 test of the Mid-Infrared Chemical Laser (MIRACL), developed under President Reagan's Strategic Defense Initiative, against a dying U.S. Air Force satellite touched off some spirited international opposition. On balance, this experiment—a test of the ability of a laser based at White Sands, N.M., to degrade the effectiveness of a satellite's optical and infrared sensors—received scant attention in the foreign media. Yet a few editors, pundits, and analysts in Western Europe and Asia condemned and belittled Washington's development of systems to paralyze enemies by depriving them of their eyes and ears in space. To them, this event clearly signaled a new round in the arms race, and to many it foretold the revival of Reagan's "Star Wars" plan.

The idea of space warfare must create in the minds of government leaders around the world vivid images of merciless domination.

The idea of space warfare must create in the minds of government leaders around the world vivid images of merciless domination by a state with the power to rain fire upon unyielding enemies. Does Washington really want to conjure this image, critics ask. Do the American people want to provoke an arms race that, in the end, could leave their homes less secure once other states follow the U.S. lead?

Prudence counsels Washington to accommodate the concerns of other governments, in this assessment. The sensibility underlying this course is time-honored. In the words of *Federalist* No. 63:

> An attention to the judgment of other nations is important to every government for two reasons: the one is that independently of the merits of any particular plan or measure, it is desirable, on various accounts, that it should appear to other nations as the offspring of a wise and honorable policy; the second is that in doubtful cases, particularly where the national counsels may be warped by some strong passion or momentary interest, the presumed or known opinion of the impartial world may be the best guide that can be followed.

The principles of sound government, therefore, demand we pay heed to foreign opinion.

Academic Assumptions

The case against deploying weapons in space rests on a number of assumptions, often unstated. A careful look at the validity of these assumptions reveals serious problems—in many cases undermining the conclusions the critics draw.

One such assumption is that military developments over the past 50 years have created a security environment in which certain tactical events or localized crises run an unacceptably high risk of triggering a general, possibly even nuclear, war. We are therefore more secure when we do nothing to upset the global military balance, especially in space—where we station key stabilizing assets.

Yet we have little experience in reality to ground this freely wielded and rather academic assumption. By definition, anything that causes instability in armed relationships is to be avoided. But would "shots" in space, any more than shots on the ground, be that cause?

When we look at what incites war, history instructs us that what matter most are the character and motivation of the states involved, along with the general balance of power (i.e., are we in the world of 1914, 1945, or 2001?). Fluctuations in national arsenals, be they based on earth or in space, do not determine, but rather more accurately are a reflection of, the course of politics among nations. In other words, it matters not so much that there are nuclear weapons, but rather whether Saddam Hussein or Tony Blair controls them and in what security context. The same may be said for space weapons.

The sway of major powers historically has regulated world stability. It follows that influential countries that support the rule of law and the right of all states to use orbits for nonaggressive purposes would help ensure stability in the age of satellites. The world is not more stable, in other words, if countries like the United States, a standard-bearer for such ideas, "do nothing." Washington's deterrence and engagement strategies would assume new dimensions with the added influence of space weapons, the presence of which could help bolster peacemaking diplomacy and prevent aggression on earth or in space.

Insofar as we have no experience in space warfare, no cases exist to justify what is in essence a theoretically derived conclusion—that space combat must be destabilizing. We do know, however, that the causes of war are rarely so uncomplicated. Small events, by themselves, seldom ever explain large-scale events. When ardent Israeli nationalist Ariel Sharon visited this past fall the holy site around the Al Aksa Mosque at Jerusalem's Temple Mount, his arrival fired up a series of riots among impassioned Palestinians and so widened the scale of violence that it kicked up the embers of regional war yet again. Yet the visit itself would have been inconsequential were it not for the inveterate hostility underlying Israeli-Palestinian relations.

Likewise, World War I may have symbolically begun with the assassination of Archduke Ferdinand in Sarajevo. Yet a serious student of history would note that the alliances, the national goals and military plans, and the political, diplomatic, and military decisions of the major European powers during the preceding years and months were the true causes of the erosion in global strategic stability. By extension, if decisions to go to war are set on a hair-trigger, the reasons for the precarious circumstances extend far beyond whether a communications or imaging platform is destroyed in space rather than on earth.

Those who believe we run extraordinary risks stemming from clouded perceptions and misunderstandings in an age of computerized space warfare might want to take a look at some real-world situations of high volatility in which potentially provocative actions took place. Take, for example, the tragedies involving the USS *Stark* and USS *Vincennes*. In May 1987, an Iraqi F-1 Mirage jet fighter attacked the *Stark* on patrol to protect neutral shipping in the Persian Gulf, killing 37 sailors. Iraq, a "near-ally" of the United States at the time, had never before attacked a U.S. ship. Analysts concluded that misperception and faulty assumptions led to Iraq's errant attack.

The memory of the USS *Stark* no doubt preoccupied the crew of the USS *Vincennes*, which little over a year later, in July 1988, was also on patrol in hostile Persian Gulf waters. The *Vincennes* crew was involved in a "half war" against Iran, and at the time was fending off surface attacks from small Iranian gunboats. Operating sophisticated technical systems under high stress and rules of engagement that allowed for anticipatory self-defense, the advanced Aegis cruiser fired anti-aircraft missiles at what it believed to be an Iranian military aircraft set on an attack course. The aircraft turned out to be a commercial Iran Air flight, and 290 people perished owing to mistakes in identification and communications.

To these examples we may add a long list of tactical blunders growing out of ambiguous circumstances and faulty intelligence, including the U.S. bombing in 1999 of the Chinese Embassy in Belgrade during Kosovo operations. Yet though these tragic actions occurred in near-war or tinderbox situations, they did not escalate or exacerbate local instability. The world also survived U.S.-Soviet "near encounters" during the 1948 Berlin crisis, the 1961 Cuban missile crisis, and the 1967 and 1973 Arab-Israeli wars. Guarded diplomacy won the day in all cases. Why would disputes affecting space be any different?

In other words, it is not at all self-evident that a sudden loss of a communications satellite, for example, would precipitate a wider-scale war or make warfare termination impossible. In the context of U.S.-Russian relations, communications systems to command authorities and forces are redundant. Urgent communications may be routed through land lines or the airwaves. Other means are also available to perform special reconnaissance missions for monitoring a crisis or compliance with an armistice. While improvements are needed, our ability to know what transpires in space is growing—so we are not always in the dark.

The burden is on the critics, therefore, to present convincing analogical evidence to support the notion that, in wartime or peacetime, attempts by the United States to control space or exploit orbits for defensive or offensive purposes would increase significantly the chances for crisis instability or nuclear war. In Washington and other capitals, the historical pattern is to use every available means to clarify perceptions and to consider decisions that might lead to war or escalation with care, not dispatch.

Drawing a Line in Space

The U.S. and Soviet experience with MIRVs is often brought up to show how Washington's "naive" foray into missile madness provoked Moscow to respond in kind. But to arrive at this conclusion, one must suspend all awareness of the strategic context surrounding the MIRV decision and assume that America had (and still has) a monopoly on knowledge. While the United States appeared to lead the Soviet Union in MIRV technology, throughout the Strategic Arms Limitation Talks of the early 1970s, which featured the MIRV negotiations, Soviet missile engineers were already busily integrating the technology into their systems. At the time, it was generally expected that Soviet planners, who demonstrated true MIRV technology as early as 1973, would fully exploit this new innovation. U.S. actions, in other words, do not deserve blame for having provoked a Soviet countereffort.

Could we stop the historical progression of weaponry at the edge of earth? From the perspective of the strategist, a "line" between outer space and the atmosphere is strictly conceptual. Nothing in the world of tactics, operations, or strategy, and nothing in the logic of deterrence or the grammar of warfare, says there must be such a line. This leaves only the possibility of political decision to make it so. But the absence of universal political will means there is no practical way to enforce supporting treaties, laws, and proclamations.

One may ask, just because the United States unilaterally refrains from developing antisatellite weapons or space-based lasers, why do we assume that other countries will pause right alongside Washington? After all, not all innovations in war stem from provocation. While weapons developed and deployed by rival states surely influence decision making, it is unlikely that states procure weapons systems primarily to achieve a balance in arsenals. Some states certainly may strive to have what we have, but they also will strive to acquire and master those weapons that meet their unique security requirements.

Washington's very reliance on satellites for security, moreover, would appear to be a more plausible motivation behind any hostile state's desire to acquire satellite countermeasures. While China might wish to integrate ASATs into its arsenal to offset Washington's deployment of ASATs as part of a deterrence strategy ("you hit one of mine, I'll hit one of yours"), Beijing is likely to be more inclined to acquire satellite countermeasures independently of what Washington does in order to degrade U.S. space advantages, which may be used to support Taiwan.

To argue that states must follow Washington and deploy space weapons out of self-interest is to ignore the fact that self-interest has many faces. In the end, foreign officials must weigh personal, national, and party priorities and strategic requirements, understand political tradeoffs, and assess whether the national treasury and domestic resources could support plans to "match" U.S. weapons. Haiti's security needs will not match those of Serbia, Iran's will not match Canada's, and India's will not match those of the United States. Space control weapons, one must conclude, would not fit very well in the defense strategies of many nations. Foreign leaders, in other words, are not automatons. Between action and reaction always lies choice.

> *There will always be attempts by foreign leaders and vocal minorities to influence U.S. procurement decisions through arms control.*

No More Coalitions?

It is further assumed that deploying arms not possessed by other states in regions unexploited by other states would put the United States in a position to coerce, even terrify, other nations. One must note, however, that Washington already has the power to tyrannize and bully with its current arsenal—but it does not. The United States deploys unparalleled—even "uncustomary"—nuclear and conventional military forces and engages in peace and combat missions on a global basis. Yet the face of overwhelming American military might neither alarms allies nor incites aggression. The U.S. retreat from several forward bases and its positive global leadership, moreover, belie suspicions that, in this unipolar world, Washington harbors imperialist ambitions.

Recent criticisms surrounding the MIRACL test and the U.S. National Missile Defense program were well orchestrated and vociferous, but numerically shallow when put up against the larger body of international opinion. In fact, voices will inevitably rise, from all corners of the globe, to condemn U.S. military decisions and actions. Political assault is the price the United States pays for having global interests and power. There will always be attempts by foreign leaders and vocal minorities to influence U.S. procurement decisions through arms control and public condemnation. It costs little, and the potential gains are great.

Would a vigorous military space program alienate foreign governments to the point at which Washington could never again assemble a coalition similar to the one that defeated Saddam Hussein in 1991? This is doubtful. Leading up to the onset of war, the Iraqi leader's actions, not President Bush's initiatives, dominated foreign policy discussions abroad. Indeed, many Arab countries joined the coalition, despite America's stout support for the much-hated Israel. Any significant anti-American rhetoric was quickly overshadowed by the singular goal of turning back naked aggression.

Similar international support may be expected in the future, even if the United States were to deploy space-based interceptors to slap down ballistic missiles aimed at New York or Los Angeles or antisatellite weapons to blind prying eyes in times of crisis or conflict. When the stakes are high and the United States must act militarily in self-defense or to protect its interests, allies and friends are likely to judge U.S. activities in space to affect politico-strategic conditions on Earth appropriately and in context.

What about the *Federalist's* advice to seek the counsel of foreign parties to help resolve domestic policy squabbles? But the *Federalist* refers to impartial advice. To be *impartial* is to view both sides of a debate equally and without prejudice or bias, as would a judge. An infant nation far distant from the powerful capitals of the late eighteenth and early nineteenth century might have little difficulty finding such counsel. Yet can we now say that in the foreign criticism thrown at the United States concerning its ASAT, ballistic missile defense, or directed energy programs, we can discern the voice of impartiality? Do we hear a voice of neutrality coming out of Beijing or Moscow? Can we declare with candor that Paris or Ottawa are sufficiently poised and disinterested to counsel Washington objectively? On this issue, politics divides hearts the world over.

Stability Revisited

Whether the vast, empty ocean enveloping earth will be traversable for military purposes and a battlefield where major political stakes are decided may be, ultimately, not a question for policy or deliberation but an inevitability. Yet having been brought up on a steady diet of bumper-sticker slogans concerning space and strategic stability, the country remains intellectually unprepared to discuss and deal with grave defense and foreign policy decisions involving space. "ASATs are destabilizing" and "space must remain a sanctuary" are punchy trumpet blasts, but they are not expressions of sober strategic thought.

A confident military power should strive to influence and be capable of controlling activities in all geographic environments affecting its prosperity and security. The United States does so on the land with its armies and border guards, at sea with a world-class navy, coast guards, and fortified bases, and in the air with fighters, bombers, and air defense assets.

Responsible leaders, it seems to follow, should strive to ensure a similar ability to influence and control activities in space. Given the increasingly commercial and international character of satellite operations, we must expect that America's public and private interests one day will be challenged or even attacked. To leave the initiative to others is to expose U.S. interests to the whims of the ambitious, the cunning, and the truculent.

A second reason for exploring new military uses of space is that they could provide our leadership and commanders life-saving options. Consider this. In fourth century BC Athens, the modern thinkers of the day proposed designing cities without traditional defenses—which included a street layout designed to confuse an invading enemy and a fortified wall around the city. Those who objected to such "old-fashioned" concepts proposed laying the streets out in tidy rows to improve the city's appearance. Removal of the costly and aesthetically offensive walls would avoid a hostile appearance that might unnecessarily provoke Athens' neighbors.

Critics of this "new thinking" believed that, while a visually pleasing and open city would be attractive, one should not adopt this approach at the expense of safety. The suggestion to remove the walls irked the more defense-minded, especially in light of the fact that the armies of the time were introducing new missiles and machines for improving sieges. The advocates for the city's strategic defenses—the walls—argued that the city's leaders would retain *the option* of treating the city as an open city, whereas the option of defense would not be available to leaders who chose to ignore the city's military requirements. Particular weapons, in other words, do not commit a country to a particular policy course; rather, they offer offensive and defensive options in a world that often punishes inflexible policies and is unforgiving of those who blunder through decisions that can make the difference between war and peace.

Finally, strength at home and assertiveness abroad have ensured stability for the United States and much of the world during the past century. Capricious misfortune and aggression, after all, are the bane of the republic—and of international security. Military strength can help the United States and its allies direct chance more favorably and, in the worst of times, deter and turn aside aggression.

Vast practical consequences will fall out of policy choices concerning the nature of American space power, especially as they affect the composition of U.S. forces, military organization, and security strategy. The new administration and Congress must help the American people overcome a habit of viewing space weapons in isolation from America's purpose. Should military requirements warrant and cost permit, space weapons could be invited to join the rest of the arsenal to secure American interests and contribute to global strategic stability.

The United States and its allies should resist enchantment with slogans that divert attention from new security possibilities, especially ballistic missile defense, which ought to be viewed in the broader context of space power. Far from jeopardizing stability and peaceful uses of space, American military power exercised on the edge of earth would contribute to world peace and freedom.

Information Warfare: Time to Prepare[5]

BY BRUCE D. BERKOWITZ
ISSUES IN SCIENCE AND TECHNOLOGY, WINTER 2000–01

During the past several years, military officials have become concerned about the possibility that a foreign adversary might strike at U.S. computers, communications networks, and databases. Although such an "information warfare" attack could be part of a larger conventional military operation, it is also possible that an adversary might use information warfare (or IW, to use the Pentagon shorthand) as a warning shot to dissuade the United States from helping an ally abroad or as part of a limited terrorist campaign.

IW presents special problems for U.S. defense planners. Many, if not most, targets of an IW attack against the United States would probably be commercial computer and communications systems. These systems are more vulnerable than those operated by the military. Commercial operators are seemingly unaware that they are potential IW targets, and few have taken any precautionary measures. Commercial software developers and hardware designers are also not attuned to the IW threat. Thanks to "Melissa," the "Love Bug," and other computer viruses, the public has become more aware of the importance of computer security. Several recent cases of cyber crime and denial-of-service (DoS) attacks have also made computer users more alert. Yet the IW threat is very different from vandalism and criminal activities.

Foreign military organizations and terrorist groups are likely to have more people and deeper pockets. They can work harder and longer on an assignment, which means that they can crack systems that might withstand an assault by a more casual opponent. They are likely to be more experienced and will use more sophisticated tactics. Most important, serious IW attackers would not reveal their activities until it is absolutely necessary. Unlike the typical hacker prankster who wants to attract as much attention as possible, sophisticated IW threats have an incentive to remain discreet and are likely to have the skills to evade detection. They would take weeks or months to lay the groundwork for an attack in secret and would then create diversions to confuse their targets so that the initial phases of an attack would be as effective as possible.

5. Reprinted with permission from *Issues in Science and Technology*, Berkowitz, "Information Warfare: Time to Prepare," Winter 2000–01, pp. 37–44. Copyright 2001 by the University of Texas at Dallas, Richardson, TX.

The dilemma for U.S. officials is that although commercial information systems are prime targets for IW attack, the government has limited influence over how these systems are designed, manufactured, and operated. The public is generally unaware of serious IW threats. It is hard to prove that a specific IW threat exists, let alone that it is planning to strike a specific target. Companies are always under pressure to reduce costs and maximize profit. All these factors make preparing for IW difficult.

> **The public is generally unaware of serious IW threats.**

But one factor makes preparing for IW harder than it needs to be. The relationship between the government and information industries has often been rocky in recent years. The two communities are often unfamiliar with each other and view their counterparts with suspicion. There is, in effect, a cultural divide between the government and the commercial sector that prevents the two communities from cooperating. Unless government officials and the information industries improve their relationship, the United States will become increasingly vulnerable as it becomes more dependent than ever on computers and the networks that interconnect them.

Commercial Vulnerability

Virtually every aspect of life has become more dependent on computers, imbedded electronics, and communications systems. All these information systems—and especially those connected to a network—are potential targets for IW attack. When defense experts talk about the IW threat to commercial information systems, they do not mean hackers or even criminals. They are referring to well-funded, sophisticated, foreign military powers, intelligence organizations, and terrorist groups. Professional military journals in several countries, including Russia and China, have discussed computer network attacks as a military option. Usually these writers refer to foreign IW capabilities and plans, but it is reasonable to assume that any military organization that has discussed foreign plans for IW has considered the option for itself.

One difficulty in preparing to defend against IW is that the capabilities for such attacks are often easy to conceal, and the best IW powers are also probably best at concealing their capabilities. Even so, one can postulate what an IW team might look like. It might consist of a force of professional computer network operators, not just a few technically savvy malcontents. These technicians will know the holes that exist in popular software packages and the slip-ups network operators commonly make in maintaining firewalls and other security measures. They will also know from their own experience the shortcuts taken by sloppy or lazy operators.

Given enough time, such an IW force could penetrate most systems connected to a public network, in part because they would have ample support. An IW team would likely have an intelligence service helping it identify the vulnerable points of an adversary's infrastructure and the computer systems they depend on. The intelligence service would also support the IW team through traditional espionage, such as stealing codebooks and passwords or planting agents who could assist an attack from inside the targeted network. IW and intelligence organizations could also work with each other to penetrate companies that produced or maintained commercial software. This would enable them to insert "trapdoors" and "Trojan horses" that they could trigger later.

In addition, the IW team would coordinate its plans with the commanders of conventional military forces. The IW team could support a conventional strike by jamming or confusing the enemy's air defense computer network, or it could magnify the effects of a military strike by hacking the databases civilian authorities need for fire and rescue operations. An IW team might spend weeks or months "footprinting" targeted computer networks; in effect, creating a mirror image of the system's design to identify its weak points. Once it had a footprint, the IW team would update its analysis regularly, as is done with any military contingency plan. With these plans in place, an IW team would be ready to go into action when needed. The potential civilian targets of an IW strike could be any communications system or computer network, or any part of a country's infrastructure that depends on such networks. For example:

- U.S. military forces depend on commercial transportation systems for logistics and, in many cases, for moving units to the scene of battle. These transportation systems depend on computer networks to control machinery, keep track of inventories, and coordinate their operations. A foreign adversary could significantly hinder U.S. forces in reaching, say, the Persian Gulf or Taiwan Straits by attacking the computers at commercial harbor facilities used to ship ammunition or the air traffic control system that would be needed to support and airlift personnel and supplies.

- The commercial broadcast systems and commercial Internet would be critical during a national emergency to coordinate public safety efforts and keep the country informed. Some of the recent virus and DoS attacks were targeted against companies such as CNN and AOL; it does not require much effort to imagine how these companies might be forced to curtail operations by a more concerted, professionally orchestrated strike.

- A serious opponent would probably target specific suppliers and companies that are especially important to either U.S. weapons production or mobilization. Attacks on small, seemingly unimportant companies might be lost in the heat of a national crisis and might be hard for such companies to detect in any case.

- Most military and government personnel use the same banks and financial institutions as the general public. If these are insecure, it would be possible for an adversary to target the data records of key individuals, either to collect compromising information or to plant disinformation.

Some writers have described how an IW attack could lead to catastrophic results: the proverbial "electronic Pearl Harbor." Such a strike might be theoretically possible, but it misses the point. IW is an inevitable byproduct of the Information Revolution. Our foreign adversaries, both regular military forces and terrorist organizations, will target U.S. information systems simply because it is possible and because it offers them another channel for effective action. As information systems become more capable, we become more dependent on them and, as we become more dependent, they will become irresistible targets. That is why we need to prepare defenses, and this requires cooperation between government and industry.

Deal with It

U.S. officials were reluctant even to discuss IW threats until the mid-1990s, when they began to understand that it was impossible to prepare for such attacks without greater public awareness of the problem. One of the first studies to discuss the threat openly was a report published by the Defense Science Board in 1996. This study, "Information Warfare—Defense" (IW-D), triggered more action. President Clinton appointed a commission under retired Air Force General Robert T. Marsh to study foreign threats to information systems and other infrastructure, such as transportation and power generation. Several of the Marsh Commission's recommendations were later enacted through Presidential Decision Directives 62 and 63, which President Clinton signed in May 1998. These directives officially acknowledged threats to the U.S. infrastructure (including cyber attacks) and proposed measures to protect it. At the same time, the president appointed a national coordinator for security, infrastructure protection, and counterterrorism to oversee the implementation of the new policies.

Several obstacles undercut these efforts, especially in their effectiveness against serious, well-supported IW threats. One problem was a result of bureaucratic politics. Agencies competed for roles in dealing with the newly acknowledged threat. The Department of Justice won the right in February 1998 to put the National Infrastructure Protection Center (NIPC) in the FBI. The NIPC was, in effect, supposed to be the federal government's command post for monitoring attacks on information systems.

Unfortunately, the FBI is a law enforcement organization. Although law enforcement organizations may be effective against hackers, criminals, and the odd troublemaker, they are ill-equipped to deal with foreign military threats and large international terrorist networks. Law enforcement organizations are designed to respond to crimes, apprehend suspects, bring them to trial, and put them in jail. Military organizations, in contrast, are designed to win wars. Both functions are important, but each type of organization operates under different rules and at a different tempo. Law enforcement is reactive and emphasizes dogged detective work. Defense is preventive, and military operations aim at ending conflicts as expeditiously as possible on terms favorable to the United States. Law enforcement requires respecting and protecting the civil rights of defendants, who are presumed innocent until proven guilty. Military operations frequently require violence

---

Law enforcement organizations . . . are ill-equipped to deal with foreign military threats and large international terrorist networks.

---

and ruthlessness to defeat (and if necessary, destroy) an adversary. It is hard to design an organization to do both, which is, in effect, what the NIPC is expected to do.

There are other problems, too. Although the military services and intelligence community have representatives at the NIPC, most of its staff comes from law enforcement organizations. Even if defense and intelligence organizations had greater representation at the NIPC, it would probably still be hard to attract up-and-coming officers to serve there. Spending a few years at a law enforcement organization monitoring hacker reports is hardly the ticket punch that gets a rising officer promoted. Also, the NIPC is not well connected into the military command system. For example, there do not appear to be clear guidelines that would define how and when a hacking incident would be determined to be a military problem rather than a criminal investigation, and how the organization would change its operation to deal with such a situation.

Meanwhile, military commanders have not concentrated on protecting commercial systems from foreign attack. They have focused mainly on ensuring that military computer systems and communications networks work. IW attacks against targets within the United States, such as state-sponsored biological and chemical weapon attacks, fall into the new mission of "homeland defense."

The military services are still not certain how to address this mission, as it is very different from the kinds of operations U.S. forces prepared for throughout the 20th century. Homeland defense requires new kinds of forces and new kinds of plans, many of which do not fit into the traditional concepts of how a military force should operate. It also raises legal issues; just as law enforcement organizations are unsuited to dealing with military threats, U.S. military forces are prohibited by statute from serving in a law enforcement function.

In addition to creating the NIPC, the federal government has undertaken several other initiatives to reduce the threat of cyber crime and cyber terrorism. Some of these involve partnerships with industry, but there are also problems that leave the government and the private sector ill-prepared to respond jointly against serious IW threats. For example, several reporting organizations have been established to share information and issue warnings about hacker attacks and computer viruses. One of the first of these was the Computer Emergency Response Team/Coordination Center (CERT/CC) at Carnegie Mellon University. CERT/CC was set up as a federally funded R&D center by the Defense Advanced Research Projects Agency in December 1988 after an early virus attack disabled 10

Homeland defense requires new kinds of forces and new kinds of plans.

---

percent of the computers then connected to the Internet. Since then, CERT/CC has effectively become the 911 number that civilian computer operators call to report such incidents. Other organizations in the United States and abroad have since established local CERTs and reporting operations. The FBI also has its Awareness of National Security Issues and Response (ANSIR) Program, which alerts industry and infrastructure operators to espionage and sabotage threats.

During its last year in office, the Clinton administration stepped up its efforts to deal with cybersecurity issues. One of its most visible initiatives was unveiled in February 2000, when the president announced he would provide $9 million in accelerated funding for computer security education programs and a new Institute for Information Infrastructure Protection. (This was to supplement $2 billion the administration had already proposed for cybersecurity initiatives in FY 2001.) The administration also planned to encourage industry to create new Information Sharing and Analysis Centers (ISACs). These centers, two of which have already been established for the financial and communications industries, are designed to allow companies targeted by hackers or cybercriminals to share information in a secure semianonymous environment. ISACs protect companies from having to disclose proprietary information when reporting such incidents and also control the flow of publicity, so customers are informed but not unnecessarily alarmed.

The problem with CERT/CC, ANSIR, ISACs, and similar programs is that they are geared to peacetime operations, not to providing wartime "indications and warning." Also, they do not routinely deal with military commands. In other words, the most likely targets for an IW strike against the United States are commercial computers and networks, and the first signs of an IW strike would likely appear in the private sector. But the reporting network that commercial operators are coming to rely on is focused mainly on pranks, crime, and natural disasters, not well-prepared terrorist or military threats. In effect, the commercial sector—our canary in the coal mine—is ill-prepared and disconnected from the organizations that would have to respond to an attack on the United States.

The Cultural Divide

It would be easier to defend against IW threats if government and industry could cooperate more effectively. Unfortunately, the two have collided on several issues recently. These clashes have undermined the more highly publicized efforts of the Clinton administration to promote public-private partnerships. Some specific points of contention have included:

- **Antitrust**. Microsoft, Intel, and America On-line have all been the targets of antitrust suits or investigation by the Department of Justice. True, computer and communications companies have long been targets of antitrust suits; indeed, the IBM and AT&T cases were landmarks. But it is hard for government to try to develop a close relationship with the new information companies with one hand, while trying to break them up with the other.

- **Encryption**. The federal government tried throughout the 1980s and most of the 1990s to regulate encryption technology. Law enforcement and intelligence agencies feared losing their ability to intercept communications. The information industry, however, believed that developing electronic commerce was impossible without strong encryption.

- **Criminal investigations**. In July 2000, the FBI became ensnared in a controversy when the press reported its use of "Carnivore," a portable computer system for implementing court-ordered intercepts of e-mail at Internet service providers (ISPs). Civil liberties groups criticized the system as an invasion of privacy. The Clinton administration, which had moved slowly on Internet privacy issues, was unprepared to explain either how the system worked or how it intended to protect the rights of e-mail users and address the concerns of ISPs.

- **Immigration**. Immigration laws have prevented IT companies from hiring the foreign talent they believe they need. This has increased their labor costs and threatened their competitiveness with foreign companies. Such restrictions also conflicted with the New Economy zeitgeist of borderless markets.

Paradoxically, from the perspective of preparing defenses against an IW strike, the government's position on all of these issues was counterproductive. Americans would probably be safer from an IW attack if U.S. companies dominated commercial markets for software and hardware, and such domination often requires a monopoly. Antitrust litigation opens opportunities for foreign competitors. (How would national security be affected if a foreign company designed the software used in U.S. banks or in popular Internet browsers?) Similarly, although encryption cannot guarantee that a commercial computer network is secure against an IW attack, it is probably impossible to make a system secure without strong encryption. Finally, immigration restrictions have encouraged U.S. companies to outsource software development to foreign countries, where there is a greater chance that it will be compromised by foreign military organizations and intelligence services.

Yet these disagreements run deeper than just quibbles over policy details. The recent disputes reflect a clash of cultures. How did this clash occur?

Part of the problem may simply be geography and history. The first-generation computer companies such as IBM, Burrows, Sperry, NCR, Control Data, and Digital were mainly based in the east and the midwest. So was AT&T, which operated as a heavily regulated government-sanctioned monopoly until its breakup in 1984. Most of these companies had long histories as contractors to the Department of Defense or other government agencies. As a result, they were accustomed to cooperating with the government, even when "cooperation" really meant following instructions. They also shared similar cultures. Many company officials had served in the military or had at least worked closely with government agencies. There were also cultural parallels: hierarchical organizations, formal rules, and even a uniform dress code at IBM.

The new companies that led the personal computer and Internet revolutions—Intel, Apple, Netscape, Oracle, and, of course, Microsoft—were different. Most took root on the west coast. Many corporate leaders had little experience with government and had never served in the military, having been born too late to be eligible for the Vietnam era draft (Bill Gates and Steve Jobs were born in 1955; Steve Case in 1958; Marc Andreessen in 1973). The new leaders often learned computers on their own and often rejected the usual course of formal education and earning professional credentials. Gates and Jobs both left college early to concentrate on business; Andreessen completed a normal stay at the University of Illinois, but once claimed he was not sure whether he received a degree or not. Their model for success was the startup and the IPO, not climbing the corporate ladder; and they believed that the consumer market was more important than government sales. Generalizations are always risky: Andreessen, for example, worked on Mosaic under government-funded research, and Larry Ellison created Oracle partly with Air Force funding. But it seems fair to say that the new corporate leaders lacked many of the government ties their predecessors had. Many see government, along with high interest rates and tight-fisted investment bankers, as just another threat that could put them out of business.

To make matters worse, the government has been losing clout. It is no longer the most important customer for computers and often does not have a lead in technology. For example, government officials could once boast that the most capable supercomputers in the world resided at the government's nuclear labs and the National Security Agency (NSA), where they were used to design hydrogen bombs and break foreign codes. Today, however, the most powerful computers available are as often in the private sector, being used, for example, by Boeing to generate three-dimensional designs for airliners or by Pixar to create animated cartoons.

The government's diminishing influence has been clear in its efforts to promote security standards for commercial information systems: a key component of any defense against the IW threat. At one time, the National Institute of Standards and Technology (NIST) could issue a standard such as the Data Encryption Standard and assume that industry would adopt it because there was nothing better. By the mid-1980s, though, some companies began offering encryption technology that approached or surpassed that offered by the government and that would have been difficult or impossible for government agencies to defeat. In 1994 the government tried and failed to convince industry to adopt Clipper, an NSA-developed encryption system that would have given law enforcement and intelligence organizations the means to break ciphers under certain legally authorized conditions. Because it was no longer dependent on the government for the best encryption and because its commercial interests seemed to diverge from the government's efforts to restrict the technology, industry refused to go along.

Government authorities have had difficulty adapting to the new situation. Even as the controversy over encryption and Clipper ensued, NSA and NIST created the National Information Assurance Partnership (NIAP) in August 1997. NIAP, a joint program to test and evaluate commercial security technology, works with industry and with standard-setting agencies in other countries.

Alas, figuring out how to negotiate and facilitate, rather than impose, industry standards has put government officials on new and unfamiliar ground. Officials are still trying to make the process work, and representatives from industry have been slow to forget that its partners were only recently opposed to any process in which they had a significant say about this key component of information security.

To be sure, the information industry was not blameless. Even as companies complained about government restrictions on encryption, most software packages designed for consumers have been designed to be easy to use, not secure. The automatic features that make popular programs easy to use also often make them easy to hack. Similarly, although companies warned that government agencies threatened the privacy of their customers for the sake of national security or law enforcement, industry often had an even more cavalier attitude toward privacy. Witness the use of "cookies" to monitor surfing habits on the World Wide Web, the selling of customer databases, and often ambiguous self-policing privacy standards. And there is the immortal quotation of Scott McNealy, chief operating officer of Sun Microsystems, who said when asked about security features in a new network software product, "You have zero privacy anyway. Get over it."

> *The automatic features that make popular programs easy to use also often make them easy to hack.*

Taking Steps

The Clinton administration's efforts during its final year to smooth relations between government and industry will help prepare the country against IW threats. Possibly the most important step was the administration's January 2000 reversal on encryption restrictions that, for all practical purposes, deregulated a key technology necessary for security against IW attack. Administration officials also began to meet more often with representatives from industry. Even so, there are several measures that the next administration should undertake that would further close the gap between the commercial sector and the government and better prepare the country for the IW threat.

The new administration must appoint officials who are willing and able to establish a better relationship with the private sector. (Lt. Gen. Michael Hayden, the current director of NSA, is an example.) Officials must appreciate that global markets will usually defeat any efforts to limit technology. Intelligence and law enforcement are always challenging tasks, and figuring out how to gain access to an opponent's communications is simply part of the job. Government agencies will probably lose any fight in which they try to maintain access to sources simply through regulation. Besides, allowing industry to develop better information security technology is not only essential to privacy and electronic commerce, it is essential to protecting the country against IW attacks.

Another step would be to concentrate on improving the private sector's understanding of the IW threat. It is impossible for any government organization to identify and fix all the vulnerabilities that may exist in the private sector's information systems. The infrastructure is too large, and there are too many restrictions on proprietary data, intellectual property, and consumer privacy that will limit the government's ability to act. Commercial software developers and network operators need to build defenses into their own systems. They need to be aware that they are the likely targets of attack, and they should have incentives to take precautions. Education is key. Colleges should be encouraged to include IW as a topic in computer science departments' curricula on information system security. Dorothy Denning, a Georgetown University computer science professor, currently offers such a course, which is a possible model. Some of the additional funding the Clinton administration proposed for cybersecurity education could be used to develop such courses. Law enforcement, military, and intelligence organizations might also make some of their personnel available to support these courses.

Commercial software developers and network operators need to build defenses into their own systems.

Industry should expand its current efforts to develop institutions that allow companies to share information about cyber attacks without compromising their customers' privacy. But an additional step is required. Industry and the Defense Department should establish operational links that will ensure that companies can work with military commanders if they are targeted by an IW strike. These links would be parallel to the existing reporting links to the NIPC, but would have a military, rather than a law enforcement, approach. There should be a clearly defined cooperative procedure that would allow military, defense, and industry representatives to reach a consensus on which mode of operations is most appropriate in a given situation.

One practical difficulty in establishing these links is that military commanders need precise, specific information that they can act on, but almost all companies would have difficulty justifying the cost of the additional people and facilities required to provide this information. There is also the always-present problem of how a company can provide information to government authorities without compromising its business interests or legal responsibilities. One approach might be for military commands to assign active or reserve officers to CERTs and the ISACs now being established. The officers would be responsible for generating the information the military commands require and would be paid by the government, but they would operate under the supervision of the civilian heads of these organizations. The relationship might also be facilitated if the military personnel provided assistance to commercial organizations in preparing their own security plans.

These links would be critical if the United States found itself under a serious IW attack. Industry would need assistance in taking defensive measures. During the summer of 2000, the U.S. Space Command was assigned responsibility for coordinating information operations by U.S. military forces, so this is where the most important connection between government and industry is required. It is especially important to develop personal relationships at the working level between people who will need to share information to respond to an attack. Exercises simulating an IW attack would give military and industry personnel a better understanding of potential threats and give them an opportunity to test and practice their response. Such exercises would also give military personnel a better appreciation of industry's concerns, and commercial operators a better appreciation of the military's concerns. Again, this is one specific activity that the proposed funding for cybersecurity education could usefully support.

The government should provide a combination of carrots (such as subsidies) and sticks (such as liability statutes defining standard accepted industry practices) to encourage commercial operators to

---

It is especially important to develop personal relationships at the working level between people who will need to share information to respond to an attack.

---

take reasonable security and privacy measures that would also protect against IW attack. For example, the level of redundancy required to ensure that a commercial computer network, communications link, or database is available during wartime may exceed the level of protection a company can justify. The government could offer programs in which it would pay for this redundancy for companies willing to participate.

Certain legislation could also help. For example, some companies are reluctant to cooperate with government on cybersecurity issues because they fear that even if officials protect their proprietary data in good faith, they may be required to release the information to comply with disclosure statutes and regulations. Some experts believe that once such information is in the possession of the government, it might be subject to a Freedom of Information Act (FOIA) request. There is some disagreement on this point, and there are already many exemptions protecting information from FOIA requests. For example, technical information that companies create under cooperative development projects with the government is exempt from FOIA, as is most information that would compromise national security if released. But legislation would make the exemptions required for cooperation on cybersecurity clear, and it is doubtful that industry will participate without such ironclad guarantees.

The Cyber Security Information Act of 2000, introduced by Reps. Tom Davis (R-Va.) and Jim Moran (D-Va.) last year, would provide these. Other legislation that would facilitate preparation against IW threats would stipulate disclosure requirements. For example, financial institutions could be required to report whether they meet industry standards for protecting their networks and data. And most legislation aimed at protecting the privacy of consumers and other users of the Internet would have the added benefit of improving security against IW.

Finally, all these institutions need to have effective oversight mechanisms to ensure the privacy of consumers. Despite recent controversies, government officials, civil liberties advocates, the information industry, and the public all need to understand that they have common interests. A system that ensures privacy is also more resistant to IW strikes and criminal attack. With a little cooperation and foresight, everyone wins.

II. Terrorism

Editor's Introduction

Although terrorism has recently emerged as the new threat to peace in the modern world, it is perhaps the oldest method of warfare. Its origins can be traced back to the 11th century, when Hassan Ben Sabbah, a Persian, gained control of much of Iran and Syria using a band of assassins he dubbed the *Fedayeen* ("men of sacrifice"). Throughout history, leaders and dictators have used terrorist tactics to achieve their goals. Today, terrorism reaches deeper into the lives of average citizens than ever before. After the horror of 9/11 came the revelation that terrorists were living in American towns in sleeper cells, working at 9-to-5 jobs and attending flight schools to learn how to turn planes into missiles. Section II explores the new face of terror by taking a stark look at these sleeper cells, as well as the growing threat to the American way of life.

In "Southeast Asia Remains Fertile Ground for Al Qaeda," Raymond Bonner examines the vast terror network that Osama bin Laden has created. Although many of Al Qaeda's activities have been disrupted by America's war on terror, sleeper cells still exist throughout the world. As Bonner explains, terrorists in Southeast Asia are turning away from such large targets as the World Trade Center and focusing on so-called "soft targets," such as resorts and night clubs. Bonner also discusses the recruitment and training these terrorists undergo.

The ever-widening grasp of the terror network is further examined in John Diamond and Kevin Johnson's article "Al Qaeda Considered as Dangerous as Before 9/11." The authors discuss how Al Qaeda operatives have gone underground, striking at selected targets with little or no warning, making their efforts very difficult to thwart. Diamond and Johnson also look at the efforts made by the Federal Bureau of Investigation, the Central Intelligence Agency, and the Defense Intelligence Agency to uncover terror cells in the United States and abroad and identify potential enemies while still upholding the constitutional rights of every American citizen.

"Suicide Terrorism" by Kaja Perina explores the psyche of the suicide bomber. One might initially judge such a person mentally ill, but Perina demonstrates that such factors as religious fanaticism and susceptibility to indoctrination may also contribute to the suicide bomber's motivation. To dismiss these bombers out of hand as insane, Perina says, is to ignore the undercurrent of religious devotion and a willingness to die for one's cause that is the driving force behind almost all terrorist activity.

Southeast Asia Remains Fertile for Al Qaeda[1]

By Raymond Bonner
The New York Times, October 28, 2002

The terrorist network that Osama bin Laden has stealthily built up in Southeast Asia over the past decade is largely intact, intelligence officials in several countries said in interviews over the last week. It may even have become more deadly and more virulently anti-American than it was a year ago, they say.

Not only that, they say, it may be harder to detect. Al Qaeda's men have become less likely to gather in camps, many of which have been bombed or closed. The main leaders of Al Qaeda's Southeast Asian network are at large, ready to activate sleeper cells, these officials said.

Consequently, Asian and Western officials in the region are virtually unanimous in expressing fears that the bombing in Bali on October 12 was a harbinger for the United States and its allies.

Previously, Al Qaeda targeted embassies and official buildings—or symbolic ones like the World Trade Center—but now these are so well protected that Al Qaeda is turning to so-called soft targets, like resorts.

A sketch of Al Qaeda's network in Southeast Asia, how it emerged and what its deadly potential is today, has been pieced together from interviews with intelligence and law enforcement officials in Indonesia, the Philippines, Malaysia and Singapore, as well as with American, Australian and European diplomats. Much of what they know comes from the interrogation of recently captured Qaeda operatives.

But as officials begin to establish a profile of the network, they realize there were many warning signs going back to the early 1990's in the Philippines and Indonesia. That is when Mr. bin Laden sent some of his most trusted lieutenants to Southeast Asia, to blend into their communities, often through marriage, while making common cause with radical Islamic groups.

The most wanted terrorist in Southeast Asia today is Riudan Isamuddin, better known as Hambali, a Qaeda operative who has been instrumental in just about every terrorist action against the United States in the region in the last 10 years. Since the Bali

---

1. Copyright © 2002 by The New York Times Co. Reprinted with permission.

bombing, which some investigators believe he masterminded, he has become the subject of an intensive manhunt by Indonesian authorities.

Officials are quick to acknowledge that their picture of Al Qaeda in Southeast Asia is incomplete, and it is as much what they do not know as what they now do that alarms them.

> *"Al Qaeda is the McDonald's of terrorism."*—**Asian official**

For example, hundreds of men in Southeast Asia have been trained at Qaeda camps, not only in Afghanistan, but also in the Philippines. "Who are they? Where are they?" asked an American intelligence official.

Although the camps used by Al Qaeda have been closed, that is little consolation to counterterrorism officials. Qaeda operatives need only a few safe houses to teach how to assemble explosives, said a Philippine intelligence officer, and houses are harder to find than camps.

To some experts, Al Qaeda looks like a multinational company, expanding its reach.

"Al Qaeda is the McDonald's of terrorism," said an Asian official. Mr. bin Laden sent his representatives to Southeast Asia and elsewhere, looking for potential franchisees, the official said. Then Al Qaeda provided the template for terrorist operations, and the local operators "were sent to Al Qaeda University in Afghanistan for training in explosives and weapons."

He described Mr. Hambali as the "managing director" for Southeast Asia. Unlike some corporate executives, he does not sit in his office, but gets out in the field and meets with his teams. As a young Islamic student in Indonesia, Mr. Hambali answered the call to fight the Soviets in Afghanistan. Then, in the early 1990's, he moved to Malaysia.

From there, he became a recruiter and travel agent for inexperienced young men who wanted to go off to Afghanistan for training, or for those with experience who wanted to fight in religious wars from Bosnia to Indonesia. He arranged for at least two of the September 11 hijackers to meet in Malaysia, in early 2000, and then travel to the United States. One of his front companies wrote a letter that allowed Zacharias Moussaoui to enter the United States. (Mr. Moussaoui is on trial in Virginia in connection with the September 11 attacks.)*

Mr. Hambali was present at the creation of what appears to be Al Qaeda's first major operational base in Southeast Asia, in the Philippines about a decade ago.

---

* Moussaoui's trial is ongoing. As of May 14, 2003, U.S. District Judge Leonie Brinkema has allowed Moussaoui, who is acting as his own attorney, access to top-secret government files to prepare his defense.—Ed.

"Every major terrorist plot by Al Qaeda against the United States has some ties to the Philippines," Zachary Abuza, a professor at Simmons College, wrote in the recently published *Tentacles of Terror: Al Qaeda's Southeast Asian Network*.

The Philippines, an overwhelmingly Catholic country, might seem like a most unlikely place to cultivate a radical Muslim insurgency. But on the southern Philippine island of Mindanao, Muslims had been waging a war for an Islamic state for 20 years, and in the 1980's, hundreds of Filipino Muslims fought against the Soviets in Afghanistan. Once they returned, they were ripe for recruiting into Mr. bin Laden's army for his new war, against the United States.

In the early 1990's, Mr. bin Laden assigned a brother-in-law, Muhammad Jamal Khalifa, to the Philippine mission. Mr. Khalifa married a Philippine woman and set up an import-export company as his cover, and to explain the movement of large amounts of money, much of it supplied by Mr. Hambali, who set up front companies in Malaysia.

Using a charity, Mr. Khalifa funneled money to two militant Muslim groups that became affiliated with Al Qaeda, the Moro Islamic Liberation Front and Abu Sayyaf. Thousands of Islamic fighters from these groups went to Afghanistan for training, and returned to fight against the Philippine government.

But separately, Mr. bin Laden set up a cell in Manila whose target was the United States. All cell members were Arabs. He entrusted the cell to Ramzi Yousef and Mr. Yousef's uncle Khalid Shaikh Mohammed, both of whom had taken part in the planning of the 1993 bombing of the World Trade Center.

Mr. Yousef was arrested in Pakistan in 1995 and is serving a life sentence in the United States. Mr. Mohammed is still at large, and is now on the Federal Bureau of Investigation's most wanted terrorist list. American officials have said that he was a key planner of the September 11 attacks.

Back in 1994, in Manila, they worked on a plan to blow up 11 American airliners over the Pacific. The plot was foiled when chemicals exploded in Mr. Yousef's Manila apartment. Helped by the network, he fled to Malaysia, where Mr. Hambali had his base, and on to Pakistan, where he was captured.

Looking back, American officials now say that Al Qaeda's Manila operations should have alerted them. "That was the real sign we should have paid attention to," a former American intelligence official in the region said.

A few months after Mr. Yousef fled, Omar al-Faruq showed up, sent by Mr. bin Laden. Mr. Faruq, who was seized in Indonesia and turned over to the Americans last June, has become a major source of information about Al Qaeda's network and operations in Southeast Asia.

Mr. Faruq had a dual mission—to work with Islamic radicals in the Philippines and to prepare terrorist attacks on American interests, Philippine officials said.

He tried to get the Moro Islamic Liberation Front and Abu Sayyaf to work together, which would have been a deadly team for Al Qaeda. But Abu Sayyaf degenerated into a group of bandits who engaged in kidnapping for ransom.

Al Qaeda's relationship with the Moro Islamic Liberation Front was more fruitful. At Mr. bin Laden's request, the front opened its Camp Abubakar to foreign jihadists, which meant they did not all have to go to Afghanistan.

Three other camps for foreigners were opened in the 1990's—Camp Palestine, primarily for Arabs; Camp Vietnam and Camp Hudaibie, for Malaysians and Indonesians. More than 1,500 Indonesians went through the camps, then returned to Indonesia, where they presumably are today, a Philippine official said.

In 2000, the Philippine Army basically demolished Camp Abubakar, and today the Moro Islamic Liberation Front is engaged in peace talks with the Philippine government.

[Omar al-Faruq] had a dual mission—to work with Islamic radicals in the Philippines and to prepare terrorist attacks on American interest.

When the Philippines became a bit less friendly, Mr. bin Laden turned more aggressively to Indonesia after Suharto fell in 1998. With more than 200 million Muslims living under a repressive government, it was ripe recruiting ground.

Once again, there was a movement for Al Qaeda to tap into, in this case Jemaah Islamiyah, which sought to establish an Islamic state across Southeast Asia. Its leader was Abu Bakar Bashir, and the chief of operations was Mr. Hambali. Last week, it was declared a terrorist organization by the United States.

In the early 1990's, American intelligence discovered that Jemaah Islamiyah was sending scores of young Muslim men to training camps in Afghanistan. When the Americans presented evidence of this to Indonesian officials, they said they were not concerned, and the United States did not push the issue, a former American intelligence official said.

In 1999, just after the repressive Suharto dictatorship was toppled, Al Qaeda set up a training camp in central Sulawesi. Hundreds of men went through the camp, including at least 200 Arabs, Indonesian intelligence officials said. The camp was closed after the September 11 attacks.

Mr. bin Laden also sent Mr. Faruq to Indonesia. There, he married an Indonesian woman and immediately hooked up with Jemaah Islamiyah.

Mr. Bashir gave money and volunteers to Mr. Faruq for terrorist plots. Working together, Al Qaeda and Jemaah Islamiyah were also plotting in the most unlikely of places, Singapore, which has the tightest security in Asia, if not the world. The possible targets included the American Embassy and other places frequented by American servicemen.

But the plot was foiled when Singaporean authorities discovered it and arrested many of the participants.

Malaysian and Singaporean authorities say they have neutralized Jemaah Islamiyah and Al Qaeda in their countries, an assessment supported by Western governments. But few other nations can make that statement with any confidence.

"It is universally accepted that the United States has done a great deal in dismantling the terrorist machine in Afghanistan," a senior Philippine intelligence official said. But, he said, "their network and contacts in Southeast Asia are still in place, and it is more radical now."

"We cannot discount the reality that these people have the capacity to do a Bali here," another senior Philippine official said.

Al Qaeda Considered as Dangerous as Before 9/11[2]

BY JOHN DIAMOND AND KEVIN JOHNSON
USA TODAY, NOVEMBER 1, 2002

U.S. intelligence and law enforcement officials say Al Qaeda has become more difficult to stop as its terrorist cells have spread out.

Disrupted by the U.S. military campaign in Afghanistan, Al Qaeda has shifted from a centralized organization to smaller, more localized terrorist cells. The cells' obscurity complicates efforts by U.S. intelligence and law enforcement to penetrate them.

As a result, officials say, the group's terrorist plots, which were not easy to uncover in the first place, have become more difficult to thwart. The current Al Qaeda is proving just as deadly as the old. The killing or capture of a few senior Al Qaeda leaders, possibly including Osama bin Laden, has not diminished Al Qaeda's ability to mount attacks against Western targets.

The group's suspected terrorist attacks in October on U.S. forces in Kuwait, in which a Marine was killed; a disco in Bali that killed at least 190 people; and on a French oil tanker off the coast of Yemen demonstrate its effectiveness.

Al Qaeda's new tactics are also forcing U.S. authorities to shift theirs. Old-fashioned police work, and the labor-intensive surveillance of hundreds of real or potential terrorists, will have to supplant military and intelligence operations as the main weapons against the new threat, officials say.

But authorities also say they face obstacles in confronting the terrorist group's new tactics:

- Although several senior Al Qaeda figures are in captivity and suspected of knowing Al Qaeda's long-term planning for attacks three to five years from now, they also are proving hard to crack. The group trains its leaders to cope with interrogation, withhold information or give false information. U.S. officials say their most reliable intelligence comes from captured documents and computer files. But obtaining such documents will be more difficult in the future when the group's agents will be scattered and not in a central location as they were in Afghanistan.

- A scattered Al Qaeda that operates in small cells will be harder to penetrate, and more intelligence agents will be needed. CIA Director George Tenet has strongly implied that the effort to enlist agents to penetrate Al Qaeda has borne fruit. Nevertheless, a senior federal official says he doubts that "any American is going to be trusted in any kind of position within the group's inner circle."

- U.S. officials sometimes feel stymied in trying to identify terrorists here. Under new law, the FBI has begun surveillance of U.S. mosques aimed at identifying recruits who might carry out Al Qaeda attacks in the USA, using their clean criminal records and anonymity as cover. But the surveillance smacks of intrusion into a religious culture and has already provoked protests from the Muslim community.

Al Qaeda's aggressive recruitment effort in the USA, focused on mosques, has paid off, according to a senior law enforcement official.

"Just like we have headhunters working the high-tech corridors for promising young executives," the official says, "Al Qaeda is

---

Travel by Muslim men to countries such as Yemen and Pakistan, where Al Qaeda has a major presence, draws the attention of U.S. intelligence.

---

doing the same thing with their own spotters and recruiters working here. That effort is strong and ongoing. The mosques have been very successful."

As a result, U.S. authorities express pessimism about their ability to consistently rout out imbedded cells manned by members with no criminal records and no dossiers in CIA terrorism files.

They predict a protracted struggle against terrorism punctuated by periodic defeats and requiring action on every front, from military to financial to legal.

Al Qaeda and other terrorist groups "retain capacity," says Army Gen. Tommy Franks, the commander and chief architect of the U.S. campaign in Afghanistan. "A lot of work remains to be done."

The Defense Intelligence Agency (DIA) reported to Congress in March in newly declassified answers to queries that the campaign in Afghanistan weakened Al Qaeda's ability to mount coordinated attacks like the September 11 suicide hijackings.

"Nonetheless," the intelligence agency reported, "experienced, at-large Al Qaeda operatives possess the ability to put together terrorist operations regardless of the ultimate disposition of senior Al Qaeda leadership."

Travel by Muslim men to countries such as Yemen and Pakistan, where Al Qaeda has a major presence, draws the attention of U.S. intelligence. In response, Al Qaeda is relying more on in-place terrorist cells and methods of attack that don't require sophisticated training. These can include crude car bombings and assassinations. Though they may be less devastating than major, coordinated strikes, they are also harder to detect.

FBI officials were relieved when no evidence turned up to support theories that the Washington-area sniper was an international terrorist. But the ease with which the sniper shootings sent the region into a panic for the better part of last month chilled federal law enforcement officials, who are only too aware of Al Qaeda's ability to watch and learn from other criminal or terrorist activity.

U.S. officials looking back on the period before the September 11 terrorist attacks say a major mistake was in viewing terrorism as a law enforcement problem as opposed to a national security problem.

More than a year later, however, federal officials are refocusing on basic police work to try to gain critical information about attacks in the planning stages. The tools of U.S. intelligence—electronic intercepts, spy satellite imagery, penetration agents—have had only limited success against Al Qaeda.

Breakthroughs, if they happen, will come from unlikely sources, Rear Adm. Lowell Jacoby, acting director of the DIA, said in testimony submitted to the intelligence committees of the Senate and the House of Representatives.

"During the pre-incident period, potential indications of terrorist activities are far more likely to be observed by police, security or bystanders than by traditional intelligence collectors," Jacoby testified on October 17. "We need to do a much better job of incorporating this type of information into our analytic equation. While 99% of it will likely turn out to be 'noise,' we cannot afford to miss the 1% that is not."

Suicide Terrorism

Seeking Motives Beyond Mental Illness[3]

By Kaja Perina
Psychology Today, September/October 2002

In 1983, when Shiite Muslims died in suicide attacks on American military barracks in Beirut, psychologists labeled them mentally unstable individuals with death wishes. Today experts agree that the acts of suicide bombers are more attributable to organizational masterminds than to personal psychopathology. Yet they continue to debate just how religion and social reinforcement transform sane human beings into sentient bombs.

Ariel Merari, Ph.D., a professor of psychology at Tel Aviv University in Israel, argues that terrorist groups such as Hamas appeal to recruits' religious piety or patriotic sentiments, but neither fanaticism nor nationalism alone are "necessary or sufficient" to foment suicide terrorism. The key ingredient may be susceptibility to indoctrination. In a recent study of 32 suicide bombers, Merari found no illuminating socioeconomic or personality factors, such as social dysfunction or suicidal symptoms. But almost all the subjects were young, unattached males, a cohort vulnerable to violent organizations in any society.

Attempts to understand suicide terrorism are understandably culture-bound. Western media emphasize a Palestinian society awash in calls to self-destruct: Iraq and Saudi Arabia pay thousands of dollars to the families of suicide terrorists, and schools teach reverence for martyrs alongside arithmetic. Palestinian mental health professionals counter that Westerners ignore the despair inherent in this logic. Mahmud Sehwail, M.D., a psychiatrist in Ramallah, says that posttraumatic stress disorder abounds among the potential—and eventual—suicide bombers he treats and cites surveys indicating that more than a quarter of all Palestinians are clinically depressed.

But the rationale of despair is a "double discourse aimed at Western audiences," according to Scott Atran, Ph.D., an anthropologist at the National Center for Scientific Research in France. "Muslims are told that these bombers have everything to live for, otherwise the sacrifice doesn't make sense." Atran's forthcoming book, *In Gods We Trust: The Evolutionary Landscape of Religion*, cites a recent study of 900 Muslims in Gaza who were adolescents during the first Palestinian *intifada* (1987 to 1993). Exposure to violence

---

correlated more strongly with pride and social cohesion than with depression or antisocial behavior. Indeed, the Gaza teens expressed more hope for the future than did a control group of Bosnian Muslims.

Ultimately, profiling suicide bombers may be a fascinating but futile psychological parlor game. Terrorism experts such as Ehud Sprinzak, Ph.D., an Israeli professor of political science, argue that the best way to halt the attacks is not to study suicide bombers themselves, but the terrorists who press these young men and women into their last, ghastly service.

III. Chemical and Biological Weapons

Editor's Introduction

C hemical and biological warfare, perhaps the most nefarious method of waging war, can trace its history back to seventh-century China, where warriors laced smoke with arsenic to form a "soul-hunting fog." During the Hundred Years War, attackers laying siege to the castle of Thun L'Evêque in Hainault, France, hurled animal corpses over the walls, forcing their opponents to surrender. In 1346 Tatars attacked the port city of Kaffa on the Black Sea, catapulting plague-infected bodies into the city. Those who fled carried the plague back to Europe, resulting in the second outbreak of the Black Death.

As threats of terrorist assaults against the U.S. and its properties overseas loom ever larger, so does the possibility of a chemical or biological attack. Anthrax has already been sent once through the U.S. mails, and reports of missing stores of smallpox, botulism, and other pathogens from abandoned research labs in the former Soviet Union abound. This section looks at this new threat from several angles.

"Russia's Poorly Guarded Past" by Joby Warrick reveals a dark underside to the Cold War, the Pokrov Biologics Plant. Warrick explains that, although Pokrov was built as a factory for animal vaccines, workers labored in secret for years to weaponize such biological agents as foot-and-mouth disease for possible use against America. After the fall of Communism, Pokrov and similar installations were deserted and their stockpiles left vulnerable to terrorists who might seize them for their own uses.

Michael Crowley's article "Combating Biological Weapons" discusses steps that are already being implemented to protect American citizens from such an attack. Crowley notes the importance of preparing doctors, pathologists, and healthcare workers, who would most likely be the "first responders" in a chemical or biological attack. He also looks at the role that the 30-year-old Biological Weapons Convention plays in the world of modern warfare.

Fighting bioterror is a costly endeavor, as Katherine Eban explains in "Waiting for Bioterror." With the U.S. healthcare system in crisis, the resources to combat such an attack simply are not there. Eban's article details how an infusion of federal funds to fight bioterror could help stem such illnesses as West Nile virus and severe acute respiratory syndrome (SARS). She also cites a disturbing example from Nevada, where an anthrax scare in 2001 led to the revelation that the state had no antibiotics to fight the disease and had to ship sample spores 500 miles away for analysis.

As with any threat, establishing a solid defense against a chemical or biological attack is the first step to overcoming it, as outlined by Steve Vogel in "A New Base for Developing Chemical, Biological Defenses." Vogel's article focuses on the Battelle Eastern Region Technology Center, a $20 million facility for developing defensive measures against bioterror. At the facility, dangerous pathogens will be examined and tested in order to develop the means to treat and curtail any outbreak that may result from a chemical or biological strike.

Russia's Poorly Guarded Past[1]

By JOBY WARRICK
THE WASHINGTON POST, JUNE 17, 2002

Bunker 12A of the Pokrov Biologics Plant is a pill factory like none other on Earth.

To enter, visitors pass through the five-ton blast doors and down the steep corridor to an underground laboratory, built of reinforced concrete to survive a nuclear attack. Inside, a few dozen workers in white coats churn out pain-relief tablets in a room lined with relics from the plant's still-secret past: 30-year-old machines used for growing viruses. Ask the plant's director about the bunker or machines and he chooses his words carefully.

"These were built," Vladimir Gavrilov says, "to handle very dangerous pathogens."

In fact, the full extent of the dangers posed by this obscure pharmaceutical factory is only beginning to be appreciated. Most of the ingredients for a biological weapon still exist here in a crumbling and poorly guarded facility that has become another front line in the battle to keep terrorists from acquiring weapons of mass destruction.

Built ostensibly as a vaccine factory for farm animals, Pokrov operated for decades as a secret within a secret: An off-the-books participant in a clandestine military program that produced the most fearsome biological weapons ever imagined. Together with a sister plant across town, Pokrov specialized in livestock maladies such as foot-and-mouth disease that could be put into weapons and unleashed on American farms in a future war, Russian and U.S. officials say. The same kinds of biological weapons are known to be coveted by Al Qaeda, the terrorist group linked last week to a plot to detonate a radiological "dirty bomb" in a U.S. city.

"Anti-livestock" or "anti-agriculture" weapons can wreak economic havoc and even undermine a nation's ability to feed itself. Under the Soviets, as many as six agricultural research centers and up to 10,000 scientists and technicians were believed to have been devoted to developing them, working under a shroud of secrecy that persists today and complicates efforts to keep dangerous materials out of the hands of terrorists, U.S. officials say.

At some of the facilities, animals weren't the only targets. Pokrov's five underground bunkers were equipped as standby production facilities that could also manufacture smallpox weapons in times of war, according to former participants in the Soviet pro-

---

gram and U.S. biodefense experts. "Pokrov could do it all," said a senior U.S. analyst familiar with the plant. "It could produce the virus . . . weaponize it and even fill the bombs."

Russia says it has halted offensive biological research and destroyed its bioweapons stockpile. There are close parallels between offensive biological weapons programs, which use lethal pathogens, and the development of defensive vaccines and other medicines using the same dangerous materials. Russia, like the United States, continues to carry out research with a wide range of dangerous microbes, developing vaccines and drugs to defend against natural outbreaks as well as acts of terrorism.

Gavrilov, Pokrov's director, said the facility is engaged only in developing vaccines and other civilian products. According to U.S. officials, the facility is believed to possess more than a dozen viruses, including Newcastle, a highly contagious disease that infects poultry and other birds.

The microbes, along with equipment needed to grow them in massive quantities, are housed in a dilapidated compound that struggles daily to do the basics: patching together its ancient alarm

---

Russia, like the United States, continues to carry out research with a wide range of dangerous microbes.

---

system, paying the arrears of its electricity bill and keeping its underpaid scientists from being lured away to other countries.

Terrorism is a constant worry. Gavrilov acknowledged there have been break-ins, as well as attempts by mysterious "Arab businessmen" to purchase various things. He said none of the attempts succeeded, as far as he knows.

"We have security concerns," the plant's director said cautiously. "But fixing them will be complicated and expensive."

Western governments have done virtually nothing to help, despite a growing awareness of the disaster that could result if terrorists acquire a single vial of the deadly microbes stored at Pokrov and more than 50 similar sites in the former Soviet Union. U.S. programs launched 10 years ago to help Russia secure its nuclear weapons have only recently begun targeting biological and chemical facilities, and progress has been slowed by money shortages and bureaucratic resistance in both countries.

Some of the largest of the former Soviet bioweapons centers, such as Vector, the onetime smallpox production complex in western Siberia, have erected fences and installed security cameras in the past three years with U.S. assistance. But at Pokrov, the first formal security assessment isn't scheduled to begin until the fall, despite two years of requests for assistance. Other bioweapons factories have yet to be visited by U.S. officials.

"On the biological side we are far, far behind," said Raymond Zilinskas, a microbiologist and bioweapons expert with the Monterey Institute's Center for Nonproliferation Studies in California. "There's a whole history of things that went on in these plants that we don't even know about."

In a country that produced the world's largest stockpiles of biological weapons, there are ample reasons to fear the unknown. Iran has made attempts to obtain Russian material and know-how for its own bioweapons programs. The same Al Qaeda leaders that plotted to explode a radioactive "dirty bomb" in the United States had an equally ambitious plan for acquiring bacteria and viruses of the kind used in Soviet weapons programs, CIA officials told Congress this year.

Former senator Sam Nunn, who has long advocated securing Soviet weapons of mass destruction as a national priority, said a brief visit to Pokrov last month was a reminder of why loose biological, nuclear and chemical material remains the "world's gravest threat."

In a country that produced the world's largest stockpiles of biological weapons, there are ample reasons to fear the unknown.

"We are in a new arms race: a race between those seeking to acquire weapons of mass destruction and those seeking to stop them," Nunn said. "Keeping dangerous things out of the hands of dangerous people is the most important thing we can do."

Even now, a decade after the Soviet Union collapsed, Pokrov's managers won't talk about the peculiar brand of agricultural research conducted there in the last decade of the Cold War.

Officially, the story is the same as it was in Soviet times: The plant produced only livestock and poultry vaccines for peaceful purposes. As a civilian institute of the Agriculture Ministry, Pokrov had no visible ties to the Soviet military.

It also had no official link to Biopreparat, the secret agency established by Soviet military leaders in the early 1970s to launch a massive biological weapons program under the guise of a network of civilian pharmaceutical plants. While Russian officials acknowledged Biopreparat's existence in the early 1990s, Moscow has never fully disclosed the contributions of other Soviet agencies, such as the Agriculture and Health ministries, to the bioweapons effort. At Pokrov, the official story begins to unravel within minutes of entering the sprawling campus 50 miles east of Moscow.

The plant's most prominent feature is a row of nuclear-hardened bunkers, an odd architectural choice for an institute concerned mostly with preventing Newcastle disease in chickens. Deputy Director Valery Stavnichy, in leading visitors through the complex, freely pointed out the bunkers' safety features, including the heavy blast doors and an underground water system that ensured uninterrupted production "in the event of emergencies."

What kinds of emergencies?

"Hurricanes. Or earthquakes," the deputy director replied. The Moscow region is not known for either.

Equally jarring to Western visitors is the scale of Pokrov's virus-making capacity. David Kelly, a British bioweapons expert who was among the first Western scientists to visit the factory, recalled his initial shock at finding bunkers filled with row after row of incubators that collectively held tens of thousands of hen eggs. "That's the standard method for growing smallpox virus," he said.

A clearer picture of Pokrov's past has recently begun to take shape from the stories of former Biopreparat officials and U.S. officials and scientists who have slowly built relationships with their Russian counterparts.

Ken Alibek, the former Biopreparat deputy director who helped expose the Soviet Union's secret bioweapons programs when he defected to the United States in 1992, said Pokrov's official role as a vaccine factory was a perfect cover for one of the biggest virus mills in the Soviet Union. If war appeared imminent, Pokrov was equipped to immediately begin production of smallpox virus at a staggering rate of 200 tons a year, said Alibek, now vice chairman and chief scientist of the Alexandria, Va., biotechnology firm Hadron Inc., in an interview.

The mobilization orders never came. But throughout their history, the Pokrov plant and its sister facility across town tested viruses for use in new types of biological weapons that targeted livestock and poultry, according to Russian and U.S. officials familiar with the program.

Igor Domaradsky, a former chairman of the Soviet Union's secret Interagency Science and Technology Council on Molecular Biology and Genetics, said Pokrov was "one of the biggest" players in an extensive network of institutes exploring anti-crop and anti-livestock weapons that could be delivered by bomb or missile. He said most of the research centered around foot-and-mouth disease, the same illness that prompted the slaughter last year of more than 4 million cows, pigs and sheep in Britain.

"Both of these [Pokrov] facilities were well equipped with a good system of sanitation and security to prevent the possibility of an escape of [viral] agents," said Domaradsky, 77, in an interview at his apartment in Moscow. "Had any escaped, it could have led to the death of many cattle, not to mention an international reaction which would have been very hard to contain."

Eventually, the Soviets abandoned most of the anti-agriculture research, primarily because of the expense and serious reservations among Soviet military planners about the weapons' effectiveness, Domaradsky said.

The retired scientist in a 1995 memoir defied Russia's scientific establishment by describing formerly secret details of Biopreparat's activities. He scoffed at what he called the "failure of memory" of Russian officials who still refuse to own up to the nation's past bioweapons activities. But whether they want to talk about it or not, he said, Russian officials must deal with the legacy of Biopreparat and Pokrov, which includes protecting some of the world's most dangerous viruses against theft.

> *There are bars on the windows in the small building where pathogens are kept.*

"Even to support vaccine production you need many different strains—a whole collection of them," he said. "And these need very tight security."

Each night at 5 p.m., as the last of the Pokrov plant's day shift boards the village bus for home, the job of protecting the factory's virus collection falls to a night watchman and a large German shepherd. The dog is judged highly capable—"he's very mean," one plant official confided—but also a poor substitute for the kind of security called for at a place that holds the seeds of multiple epidemics.

If the dog is reliable, that is more than Pokrov can claim for the rest of its security apparatus.

The plant's alarm system is 30 years old, and officials acknowledge it no longer works in parts of the campus, which is overrun with weeds and littered with debris. The military garrison once assigned to Pokrov is gone, and today's guards are mostly old men. A visitor recently saw no sign the guards were armed.

There are bars on the windows in the small building where pathogens are kept. But once inside, security for the virus freezers consists of a simple lock and a string with a seal of soft clay. A disturbed seal is a signal that viruses may have been tampered with—presumably after the thief has gotten away.

Lawrence Renteria, a Virginia-based security contractor who is helping several former weapons plants improve their systems, said Pokrov is in better shape than some.

"It isn't pretty," said Renteria, senior system engineer for Stratford Technology of Montross. "At one plant we visited, security consisted of two fat guys in sweat pants. They say they patrol the plant. But we know they don't."

Officials at Pokrov are acutely aware of the problems with security but said they lacked the money to fix them. Four years ago, the plant ran out of money for its staff, some of whom worked for up to six months without a paycheck, which was common in Russia during the 1990s. Today Pokrov pays workers the equivalent of $65 a month, with senior scientists earning about $145.

Pokrov director Gavrilov is eagerly courting Western firms for potential joint ventures that could help pay for new equipment. He also is waiting for U.S. officials to deliver on a two-year-old promise to install a modern security system.

The delay, U.S. officials explained, is due to competing demands on the limited money Congress sets aside each year to help protect and dismantle Soviet weapons of mass destruction. Funding for the Cooperative Threat Reduction Program, established by Nunn and Sen. Richard G. Lugar (R-Ind.) in 1991, has remained essentially flat in recent years, and had been targeted for deep cuts before the September 11 attacks.

For most of the past decade, greater emphasis was placed on safeguarding nuclear materials and physically dismantling strategic weapons such as the massive Soviet submarines that could launch

---

Officials acknowledge the U.S. efforts were relatively slow to recognize the threat posed by biological and chemical weapons facilities in the former Soviet Union.

---

nuclear missiles. Officials acknowledge the U.S. efforts were relatively slow to recognize the threat posed by biological and chemical weapons facilities in the former Soviet Union.

Despite substantial progress, the U.S. programs have managed to provide security upgrades for only about 40 percent of Russia's nuclear facilities, and a much smaller percentage of biological and chemical sites. Lugar, who is pressing for legislation to expand the program, said at the current rate it will be 27 years before some Russian facilities are fully secure.

"If someone gets their hands on just one of these weapons of mass destruction, the horror will be so awesome that all of life will change substantially," Lugar said during a visit to Russia in May. "If we do not take the leadership and take it aggressively, heaven help the rest of the world."

In the western Siberian town of Koltsovo, 1,800 miles east of Pokrov, Russia's only authorized smallpox research facility scarcely worries about intruders. The former bioweapons complex known as Vector is now ringed by three brand-new fences and a network of the latest Western-made cameras and motion sensors.

Troops armed with assault rifles patrol the entrances, stopping and searching each vehicle that arrives or departs from the State Research Center for Virology and Biotechnology, as Vector is formally known. These days, many of the vehicles carry Western businessmen and scientists involved in one of nearly 50 joint ventures currently underway here.

Lev Sandakhchiev, a biologist who now serves as director, acknowledged that new fences have not solved all of Vector's problems. But the heavy U.S. and European presence here appears to have eased multiple security concerns—including the fear that Iran would steal Vector's microbes or expertise.

"We no longer hear about the Iranians here," said one senior U.S. official who spoke on condition of anonymity. "We know they are active in other places—the second-tier places—but not at facilities where we have influence."

It almost didn't turn out that way. As recently as 1998, Iran was aggressively wooing Vector's top scientists and officers, proposing cooperative ventures intended to enhance Tehran's biological capabilities, said Yuri Klimov, Vector's financial director.

Klimov said he was one of several Vector officials invited to visit Tehran to explore business opportunities—an invitation he accepted. Describing the encounters in an interview outside Vector's front gate, the natty, powerfully built Klimov said the Iranians turned up at a time of great uncertainty for the institute, which was then struggling to find its niche amid Russian economic chaos and a newly competitive business climate.

"They invited some of our scientists to go to Tehran. I myself went there twice," Klimov said. "They offered our scientists $5,000 a month—a very good salary."

The Iranians were vague about their intentions, even with their Russian guests in Tehran, he said.

"They talked about arranging a joint research facility, and they were interested in technologies that we had, especially our expertise in virology," he said. "To be honest, I never understood it. And they would never directly answer our questions."

All the scientists eventually returned to Russia, Klimov said, and further contact with the Iranians was halted—for the simple reason that newly arriving Western scientists were making a better offer.

"This was the same time when we began to arrange research contacts with the United States," he said. "Ultimately we made a decision to go that way instead."

Combating Biological Weapons[2]

By Michael Crowley
UN Chronicle, July/August 2002

The tragic events of 11th September, coupled with the subsequent anthrax attacks and hoaxes, have greatly increased global concern over the risk of biological warfare, particularly bio-terrorism. However, the international community's attempts to strengthen the prohibition of biological weapons (BW) by negotiating a legally binding verification Protocol to the 1972 Biological Weapons Convention (BWC)—Convention on the Prohibition of the Development, Production and Stockpiling of Bacteriological (Biological) and Toxin Weapons and on their Destruction—foundered when the United States rejected the draft text at the July 2001 Ad Hoc Group negotiating meeting. This setback was reinforced and deepened at the fifth BWC Review Conference in 2001 when the United States called for the disbandment of the Group.

The United States position, taken as a result of its concerns over national security, corporate intellectual property rights and enforceability, has left unclosed a dangerous gap in the international control regime. What might then be done to make BW proliferation and use less likely? What role can the United Nations play in combating biological weapons? In discussing initiatives, it is important to examine areas where it might be possible to engage the United States Administration, and to build upon, expand and internationalize the elements of its proposals.

Tackling the BW threat should be a key priority for the United Nations over the coming years, as the likely consequences of inaction are stark. As Secretary-General Kofi Annan told the General Assembly on 1 October 2001: "It is hard to imagine how the tragedy of 11 September could have been worse. Yet, the truth is that a single attack involving a nuclear or biological weapon could have killed millions."

This article sets out the case for increasing the role of the UN system in BW control in four specific areas: supporting the BWC and enabling State compliance; criminalizing breaches of the Convention; disease surveillance and humanitarian assistance; and facilitating verification of compliance.

The case for reinforcing the BWC by establishing supportive institutions to promote adherence to the Convention has been raised repeatedly by its States parties, most recently at the adjourned 2001 Review Conference. The United Nations, particularly its

---

Department for Disarmament Affairs (DDA), could well play a key role if such structures came into being. It has been envisioned that such interim supportive institutions[1] would comprise a representative committee of oversight formed from and mandated by the BWC Review Conference, and supported by scientific and legal advisory panels, and a small, dedicated secretariat. These bodies would be "interim" because their initial mandate would run only to 2006, when the Sixth Review Conference might amend or renew it; and "supportive" because they would support the effective operation of the Convention on behalf of the States parties collectively. They would give the BWC a focal point and continuity of attention in the five-year intervals between its Review Conferences. Possible roles for an interim committee of oversight and a secretariat could include:

- overseeing the effective application of the Convention and, in particular, following up the Review Conference's Final Declaration and decisions, and assisting States parties in implementing them;

- overseeing the operation of, and assisting States in complying with, the politically-binding information exchange confidence-building measures (CBMs), first introduced by the second Review Conference in 1987;

- facilitating the dissemination of information, such as Review Conference documentation, lists of States parties, CBMs, etc.; and

- promoting universal adherence to the Convention and facilitating accession of States that are not yet parties to the Convention.

The circulation of CBM information could lead to the development of best practices in domestic legislation prohibiting BW production and development. Such convergence would, in turn, facilitate the development of international controls. Though all CBMs are politically-binding commitments, they have been, at best, only patchily implemented.

Very few States parties have consistently fulfilled their requirements,[2] even though a simplified reporting procedure for the CBM programme has been in operation since April 1992, and each Review Conference has called for their adherence. DDA, which holds copies of all CBMs submitted by States, is well placed to act as a facilitator and resource body aiding greater State compliance with reporting.

Source: www.militaryphotos.net

Similarly, despite continued appeals at successive BWC Review Conferences, only 144 countries (roughly 75 per cent) are parties to the Convention. Of the non-party States, 18 have signed but have not ratified, whilst a further 30 have not yet signed. While some States, especially in the Middle East, have been resistant to joining the BWC because of regional security concerns, for many others inadequate resources or political will have been the main stumbling blocks. The path to ratification or accession could therefore be eased by a helpfully persistent oversight committee and a secretariat with requisite legal resources. These bodies could likewise facilitate and encourage those States still with official reservations to the 1925 Geneva Protocol[3] prohibiting the use in war of chemical and biological weapons, such as retaining a "right" of retaliatory use of biological weapons, to withdraw them.

In the run-up to the BWC Review Conference, President George Bush called on State parties to "enact strict national criminal legislation against prohibited BW activities with strong extradition requirements." Although such criminalization would be an important development, it would not be enough. For it is doubtful whether all States would enact appropriate penal legislation, leaving safe havens where BW users could seek sanctuary. Furthermore, there is a danger that disparities in the detail of such legislation may lead to inconsistencies between national jurisdictions. What is needed is a universal criminalization of individual involvement in biological weapons by making such activities international crimes.

A treaty to create such law has, in fact, been drafted by the Harvard Sussex Program, in consultation with an international group of legal authorities.[3] This proposed treaty would make it an offence for any person—including government officials and leaders, commercial suppliers, weapons experts and terrorists—to order, direct or knowingly render substantial assistance in the development, production, acquisition or use of biological or chemical weapons. Any person, regardless of nationality, who commits any of the prohibited acts would face the risk of prosecution or extradition should that person be found in a State that supports the proposed convention. Such individuals would be regarded as *hostes humani generis* (enemies of all humanity). The development of international criminal law to hold individuals responsible would create a new dimension of constraint against biological weapons. The norm against using biological agents for hostile purposes would be strengthened; deterrence of potential offenders, official and unofficial, would be enhanced; and international cooperation in suppressing the prohibited activities would be facilitated.

The legal organs of the United Nations would, of course, have a crucial role to play in such treaty development. It is important therefore that relevant UN bodies examine the Harvard Sussex draft treaty and give consideration to initiating a process to develop a legal instrument to ensure that breaches of the BWC are treated as an international crime.

Preparing for biological warfare or terrorism has more in common with confronting the threat of emerging infectious disease than preparing for chemical or nuclear attacks. An appropriate defense against potential BW attack, whether covert or overt, by State or non-State actors must be based on improved health surveillance and response. The "first responders" for a biological attack would most likely be doctors, pathologists and other health care workers, and the speed of a response will depend on their recognition that certain illnesses appear out of the ordinary.

The "first responders" for a biological attack would most likely be doctors, pathologists and other health care workers.

Regardless of whether the origin of a disease outbreak is intentional (terrorism or warfare), accidental or natural, a public health response will be necessary to detect and contain it. Moreover, such a capability will benefit the host population whether or not a BW attack ever occurs. This is a crucial area where there is growing consensus among the international community of the need to act in concert. The United Nations and its specialized agencies, particularly the World Health Organization (WHO), working together with the BWC States parties, have a crucial role to play in combating biological weapons in the context of disease prevention. Whilst some important initiatives have been undertaken, above all by WHO,[4] the level of national and international preparedness, coordination and resourcing could be much improved, specifically in the development and coordination of global disease surveillance, awareness and preventative measures and of response to BW attack and provision of humanitarian assistance.

First, UN agencies have as yet underutilized vital coordination roles in assisting States parties to strengthen national and local programmes of surveillance for infectious diseases and in improving early notification, surveillance, control, protection and response capabilities. Such coordination might include promoting the exchange of scientists and experts to enhance the capability of States parties in supporting their surveillance programmes and increased operation, and coordination and access of existing databases on infectious disease.

Second, UN agencies can play a vital role in responding to BW attacks. WHO, for example, could coordinate rapid provision of medical assistance, while the Food and Agriculture Organization of the United Nations could provide assistance with the Office International des Épizooties (World Organization for Animal Health) if the attack was made on plants or animals, rather than human targets. Furthermore, where local resources are insufficient to cope with the humanitarian aspects of the situation, then the UN Office for the Coordination of Humanitarian Affairs could also be called in.

The last critical area where the United Nations has an absolutely central role to play is in the coordination and expression of mechanisms for ensuring compliance of the BWC. The first activity and one that has been successful in the past is international compliance diplomacy. The General Assembly, Security Council and Secretary-General have played crucial roles in encouraging State adherence to the BWC, the Geneva Protocol and the general norm of BW prohibition. Where such compliance is in doubt, the UN diplomatic corps has a vital role in establishing how such concerns should be addressed by the mutual consent of all parties. However, there will be cases where such diplomacy fails and where there will be a need for an effective investigatory mechanism to determine compliance with the BWC and the general prohibition on biological weapons. This was recently voiced in the draft Final Declaration of the 2001 Review Conference, which stated: "The Conference invites States parties to consider the development by all States parties of a compliance mechanism within the framework of the Convention to conduct investigations regarding alleged breaches of the Convention."

Although the United States currently rejects further negotiation of a legally binding BWC verification Protocol, it called for the establishment of voluntary compliance mechanisms, as well as for international investigations of suspicious disease outbreaks and/or alleged BW incidents. Under this proposal, parties would be required to accept international inspectors upon determination by the Secretary-General that an inspection should take place. Under Article VI of the BWC, a mechanism establishing a Security Council investigation system already exists, although it has never been utilized.

Considering the widespread concern that certain States have undertaken research and development of biological weapons, we must ask ourselves why Article VI has never been invoked? Why, for example, did the United States refuse to invoke Article VI against the six nations it accused of BW research and development at the Review Conference? Part of the reason may lie in the perception that the Security Council, and by extension the office of the Secretary-General, are heavily constrained from acting by geopolitical considerations and the requirement of Council consensus.

Similar concerns were also raised in the context of the operation of the United Nations Special Commission (UNSCOM), established in 1991 after the Iraq-Kuwait war with the aim of eliminating Iraq's weapons of mass destruction and ballistic missile delivery systems. UNSCOM succeeded despite continual and increasing Iraqi obstruction and evasion, but suffered from two critical weaknesses. First, questions were raised by Iraq and other States over its impartiality, culminating in allegations that UNSCOM members had been spying for the United States. Second, while its mandate and power to act came from the UN Security Council, over the subsequent nine years unanimity was eroded to the point where Council agreement on action could not be achieved.

Unfortunately, the United States proposal for a Secretary-General's investigatory regime is likely to suffer from the same failings. What is needed is a truly independent compliance monitoring and verification regime, whether inside the UN system or one along the lines elaborated in the Protocol negotiations.

In some future situations, the international community may well have to deal with sustained and deliberate attempts by a State party to develop and maintain biological weapons in direct breach of its commitments under the BWC. Such a regrettable state of affairs will provide a powerful test of both the multilateral approach to BW control and the role of the UN within this system. Dealing with such challenges, it will be crucial that the international community focus its enforcement efforts through the United Nations. Despite the difficult consensus-building that such an approach would involve, it would ensure the vital moral and legal legitimacy necessary for prolonged action against another State party. As Kofi Annan put it in his Millennium Report, the UN remains "the only global institution with the legitimacy and scope that derive from universal membership." As such, it must remain central to all efforts at international BW prohibition enforcement.

Notes

1. See Nicholas Sims, "Nurturing the BWC: Agenda For The Fifth Conference and Beyond," *CBW Conventions Bulletin*, no. 53, September 2001; *Disarmament Diplomacy*, no. 58, June 2001; "Interim supportive institutions for the Biological Weapons Convention," presented at the 14th workshop of the Pugwash Study Group on the implementation of the Chemical and Biological Conventions, 18 November 2000.

2. A study found that by 1996, only 75 of the BWC States parties had taken part even once since 1987, and only 11 had made annual declarations as required. See Marie Isabelle Chevrier, "Doubts About Confidence: The potential limits of Confidence-Building Measures for the Biological Weapons Convention," in Amy Smithson (ed.), *Biological Weapons Proliferation: Reasons for Concern, Courses of Action*, Stimson Centre Report, no. 24, 1998.

3. See Matthew Meselson, "Averting the exploitation of biotechnology," Harvard-Sussex Program (*http://www.fas.org/bwc/papers/junemesel.htm*); "Strengthening the Biological Weapons Convention," *CBW Conventions Bulletin*, no. 42, December 1998 (*http://www.fas.harvard.edu*); and "International Criminal Law and Sanctions to Reinforce the BWC," *CBW Conventions Bulletin*, no. 54, December 2001 (*http://www.fas.harvard.edu*).

4. The WHO, for example, is trying to improve the situation with such initiatives as the Global Outbreak Alert and Response Network. Established in April 2000, it links 72 existing networks around the world, many of which are equipped to diagnose unusual agents and handle dangerous pathogens.

Waiting for Bioterror[3]

By lKATHERINE EBAN
THE NATION, DECEMBER 9, 2002

Just before the July 4 holiday this past summer, as National Guardsmen with sniffer dogs monitored the nation's bridges and airports, Jerome Hauer, an assistant secretary at the Health and Human Services Department, dispatched a technician to Atlanta to set up a satellite phone for the new director of the Centers for Disease Control.

If smallpox broke out, if phones failed, if the federal government had to oversee mass vaccination of an urban center, Hauer would have a way to communicate with the CDC director, who since last fall has worked with him on health crises, particularly bioterror. It was one of many precautions that might make the difference between a manageable event and full-scale disaster.

But at the same time, an attempt at crisis management of a more immediate kind was unfolding 2,500 miles to the west. As the FBI chased reports of potential new threats, including a possible attack on Las Vegas, Dr. John Fildes, the medical director of Nevada's only top-level trauma center, watched helplessly as a real medical disaster developed, one that had nothing and everything to do with the problems that Hauer was working to solve.

Faced with a dramatic spike in the cost of their malpractice insurance, fifty-seven of the fifty-eight orthopedic surgeons at University Medical Center in Las Vegas resigned, forcing the state's only trauma center that could treat it all—from car crash, burn and gunshot victims to potential bioterror casualties—to close for ten days.

With Las Vegas a potential target, a quarter-million tourists at the gaming tables and the closest high-level trauma center 300 miles away, the crisis barely registered in the federal government. Nevada's Office of Emergency Management called to inquire about a backup plan, which, as Dr. Fildes later recounted, was to dissolve the county's trauma system, send patients to less prepared hospitals and take the critically injured to Los Angeles or Salt Lake City, both about eighty minutes by helicopter.

During that anxious week Hauer's satellite phone and Fildes's resignation letters formed two bookends of the nation's disaster planning. Hauer—whose Office of the Assistant Secretary for Public Health Emergency Preparedness (ASPHEP) was created by the

---

3. Reprinted with permission from the December 9, 2002, issue of *The Nation*.

department Secretary, Tommy Thompson, after the anthrax attacks—can get a last-minute satellite phone, a crack staff and even the ear of President Bush on public health concerns.

But Fildes, whose trauma center is the third-busiest in the nation and serves a 10,000-square-mile area, struggles to keep his staff intact and the doors of his center open. And this is in a state with no appointed health director, few mental health facilities, no extra room in its hospitals and the nation's only metropolitan area, Las Vegas, without a public health laboratory within 100 miles. In the event of a public health disaster, like a bioterror attack, Fildes says, "We're prepared to do our best. And I hope our best is good enough."

A Public Health "Train Wreck"

On taking office, President Bush eliminated the health position from the National Security Council, arguing that health, while in the national interest, was not a national security concern. In the wake of the anthrax attacks last year, he changed his tune, declaring, "We have fought the causes and consequences of disease throughout history and must continue to do so with every available means." Next year's budget for biodefense is up 319 percent, to $5.9 billion. States, newly flush with $1.1 billion in biodefense funds, have gone on shopping sprees for emergency equipment like gas masks, hazmat suits and Geiger counters. Newly drafted to fight the war on bioterror, doctors and public health officials are now deemed vital to national security, and their hospitals are even under threat, according to an alert released in mid-November by the FBI.

And yet this flurry of interest and concern has not begun to address America's greatest public health vulnerability: the decrepit and deteriorating state of our healthcare system. In states from Nevada to Georgia, dozens of health officials and doctors told *The Nation* that anemic state funding, overcrowding and staff shortages may be greater problems in responding to bioterror than lack of equipment or specific training. "We don't have enough ER capacity in this country to get through tonight's 911 calls," said Dr. Arthur Kellerman, chairman of the emergency medicine department at the Emory University School of Medicine in Atlanta. Two decades of managed care and government cuts have left a depleted system with too few hospitals, overburdened staff, declining access for patients, rising emergency-room visits and an increasing number of uninsured. The resulting strain is practically Kafkaesque: How do you find enough nurses to staff enough hospital beds to move enough emergency-room patients upstairs so that ambulances with new patients can stop circling the block?

The infusion of cash for bioterror defense without consideration of these fundamental problems is like "building walls in a bog," where they are sure to sink, said Dr. Jeffrey Koplan, the recently departed head of the CDC.

Between 1980 and 2000, the number of hospitals declined by 900 because of declining payments and increased demands for efficiency, according to the American Hospital Association, leaving almost four-fifths of urban hospitals experiencing serious emergency-room overcrowding. Burnout and low pay have left 15 percent of the nation's nursing jobs unfilled, and the staffing shortage has led to a drop in the number of hospital beds by one-fifth; in Boston by one-third, according to the Center for Studying Health System Change in Washington.

Meanwhile, emergency room visits increased by 5 million last year, according to the American College of Emergency Physicians. One in eight urban hospitals diverts or turns away new emergency patients one-fifth of the time because of overcrowding, the American Hospital Association reports. And the costs of health insurance and medical malpractice premiums continue to soar.

In public health, chronic underfunding has closed training programs and depleted expertise. According to a recent CDC report, 78 percent of the nation's public health officials lack advanced training and more than half have no basic health training at all. During the anthrax crisis inexperienced technicians in the New York City pub-

---

Only 20 percent of the nation's 3,000 local public health departments have a plan in place to respond to bioterror.

---

lic health laboratory failed to turn on an exhaust fan while testing anthrax samples and accidentally contaminated the laboratory.

A government study of rural preparedness this past April found that only 20 percent of the nation's 3,000 local public health departments have a plan in place to respond to bioterror. Thirteen states have had no epidemiologists on payroll, said Dr. Elin Gursky, senior fellow for biodefense and public health programs at the ANSER Institute for Homeland Security. Meanwhile, 18 percent of jobs in the nation's public health labs are open, and the salaries create little hope of filling them. One state posted the starting salary for the director of its public health laboratory program—a Ph.D. position— at $38,500, said Scott Becker, executive director of the Association of Public Health Laboratories. Becker calls the combination of state cuts and workforce shortages a "train wreck."

Amid this crisis, clinicians have a new mandate: to be able to fight a war on two fronts simultaneously. They must care for the normal volume of patients and track the usual infectious diseases while being able to treat mass casualties of a terrorist event. They now have some money for the high-concept disaster, but with many states in dire financial straits, there is less money than ever for the slow-motion meltdown of the healthcare system, in which 41 million

Americans lack health insurance. In the event of a smallpox attack, the tendency of the uninsured to delay seeking treatment could be catastrophic.

Hauer hopes that the "dual use" of federal resources could herald a golden age in public health, with tools for tracking anthrax or smallpox being used also to combat West Nile virus or outbreaks from contaminated food. But politicians of all stripes continue to propose beefing up biodefense in isolation from more systemic problems. In October, Al Gore argued in a speech that the problem of the uninsured should take "a back seat" temporarily to the more urgent matter of biodefense. And Bush has proposed shifting key public health and biodefense functions into his proposed Department of Homeland Security, a move likely to weaken daily public health work like disease surveillance and prevention, according to the General Accounting Office. A bipartisan report recently issued by the Council on Foreign Relations warned that America remains dangerously unprepared for a terrorist attack, with its emergency responders untrained and its public health systems depleted.

The solution, say doctors, is to tackle the systemic and not just the boutique problems. "If you have a health system that is chaotic and has no leadership and is not worried about tuberculosis and

---

America remains dangerously unprepared for a terrorist attack.

West Nile and just worried about these rare entities, you'll never be prepared," said Dr. Lewis Goldfrank, director of emergency medicine at Bellevue Hospital Center in New York City. "To be useful, money has to be earmarked for public health generally, so that it will prepare you for terrorism or naturally occurring events."

President Bush strongly resisted federalizing airport security until it became clear as day that private security companies and their minimum-wage workers would continue to let a flow of box cutters, knives and handguns through the metal detectors. Some clinicians now say that the specter of bioterror raises a similar question, which almost nobody in Washington has yet begun to address: Has healthcare become so vital to national security that it must be centralized, with the federal government guaranteeing basic healthcare for everyone?

"Forget about paying for the smallpox vaccine," said Dr. Carlos del Rio, chief of medicine at Atlanta's Grady Memorial Hospital. "Who's going to pay for the complications of the vaccine? With what money? We haven't even addressed that. As you look at biot-error issues, it's forcing us to look at our healthcare delivery."

Crisis Management in Crisis

Hauer spends much of his time in a windowless set of offices within the vast Health and Human Services Department, trouble-shooting the medical consequences of a hypothetical dirty bomb or intentional smallpox outbreak. He must also navigate the knotted bureaucracy of forty federal agencies that respond to terrorism, twenty of which play some role in bioterror response, and guide the states through infrastructure problems so severe they boggle the mind. His tactic at a meeting in Washington this August with state emergency managers was to put the fear of God into them. In the event of mass vaccinations for smallpox, the logistics are "very daunting," he told the small and sleepy group in a conference room at the Mayflower Hotel. "They will fall on emergency management, and the health departments will turn to you and say, 'You need to open 200 vaccination centers.'"

This seemed to focus the group. Before Hauer got up, these local and regional representatives had been talking about lessons learned from managing hurricanes and the best kinds of handheld chemical-weapons detectors.

Tommy Thompson created Hauer's office after the CDC, then his lead agency on bioterror, appeared to bungle the anthrax response and the Administration found itself in a scientific and logistical quagmire. Some officials claimed the White House muzzled the CDC. Others accused the CDC of sloth and bad science for failing to realize quickly that anthrax spores can leak from taped envelopes. Hauer seemed like a good choice to find a way out of this mess: He had developed the nation's first bioterrorism response plan as director of New York City's Office of Emergency Management under Mayor Rudolph Giuliani.

Hauer told the group that his office had moved $1.1 billion to the states in ninety days and was now doing audits, offering technical assistance and helping to stage drills.

But it was the nitty-gritty of mass vaccination that really quieted the room. Training a vaccinator usually takes two hours, though it can be done in fifteen minutes; for every million people vaccinated, about two will die; the vaccinators need to be federally insured because of liability; and all those vaccinated must keep the vaccination site unexposed to others for up to twenty-one days. Who would pay the salaries of contract workers on their days off?

Few emergency managers seemed to have considered such problems. Most were still immersed in competing disaster plans and state budget battles, coping with teetering local health departments and vendors hawking "equipment that will detect the landing of Martians ten miles away in a windstorm," as James O'Brien, emergency manager for Clark County, Nevada, put it.

Hauer returned that afternoon to just such a morass: figuring out how to create a unified command for the national capital area, encompassing Maryland, Virginia and the District of Columbia, seventeen jurisdictions over 3,000 square miles, with embassies, consulates, the World Bank and the International Monetary Fund. He had assigned this problem to a team from the Office of Emergency Response (OER), the federal office under ASPHEP that coordinates medical resources during disasters, who arrived at his office to report their progress.

Each state, unsurprisingly, wanted to be the lead responder, and the team recommended that Hauer try to break the logjam and give direction. He pored over the list of those invited to a coordinating committee meeting—twenty-nine people from twenty-nine different agencies—and concluded, "We need to come away with plans, not some loosie-goosie love fest where everyone pats each other on the back and jerks each other off."

The OER team trooped out with its marching orders and the next meeting began. The CEO of the New York Blood Center, Dr. Robert Jones, with a DC consultant in tow, came to ask for money to expand the center's program of making umbilical cord (placental) blood, used for patients exposed to massive radiation. Jones said the center already had about 18,000 units of cord blood stored in "bioarchive freezers" on First Avenue in Manhattan.

"You might want to think about storing it away from Manhattan," said Hauer, suggesting the obvious, as he got out a little booklet and looked up a one-kiloton nuclear bomb. "You'd need 20,000 to 40,000 units" to begin treating a city of people, said Hauer. "What's the lead time for getting it into a patient?"

Jones, who had never met Hauer before, seemed surprised to be taken so seriously and to be crunching numbers about three minutes into the conversation. Hauer, wanting to stockpile cord blood, seemed surprised that Jones had not brought a written proposal with a dollar amount. This was no time to be coy about asking for money.

Suddenly Hauer's secure phone rang and the room fell silent. "This is Jerry Hauer," he said. "You have the wrong number."

Leaving Las Vegas—in the Lurch

In Las Vegas, a gaming town with an appetite for risk, little by way of a medical infrastructure ever developed. With the population exploding and 6,000 families a month moving into the Las Vegas area in Clark County, population 1.4 million, it is also dramatically short on hospitals. By a thumbnail calculation—for every 100,000 people you need 200 beds—the county, which has eleven hospitals, is 600 beds short, said Dr. John Ellerton, chief of staff at University Medical Center, where the trauma center closed.

Even if you build more hospitals, how would you staff them? The state ranks fiftieth in its nurse-to-patient ratio, and because of the malpractice crisis, ninety of the state's 2,000 doctors have closed their practices and another eighty-three said they have considered leaving, according to Lawrence Matheis, executive director of the Nevada State Medical Association. The overcrowded emergency rooms are closed to new patients 40 percent of the time. Paramedics often drive and drive, waiting for an open emergency room. In turn, patients can wait four hours for an X-ray, three for a lab test. "There is no surge capacity, minimal staffing, minimal equipment," said Dr. Donald Kwalick, chief health officer of Clark County. "Every hospital bed in this county is full every day."

At times, the populace and even the doctors have seemed strangely indifferent. One night this summer an ambulance crew from the private company American Medical Response got called to a casino, and as they wheeled a stretcher amid the gaming tables, not a single patron looked up. Their patient: a man with a possible heart attack slumped over a slot machine. "The purity of our devotion to individual liberties tends to diminish our security and humane concern," said Matheis.

The September 11 attacks did not entirely transform this mindset. Since 1998 the city had been included on a federal government list of 120 cities that should prepare for possible attack. Eleven of the world's thirteen largest hotels, one with more than 5,000 rooms, are here. But this August, even the president of the state's medical association, Dr. Robert Schreck, said he worried little about terrorism. Al Qaeda's intent is "to kill capitalism," he said, sipping wine in the lobby of the elaborate Venetian Hotel, home to a massive casino and dozens of stores. "Why would they hit us?"

But last year Nevadans began to lose their cool as the medical system disintegrated. As malpractice insurance premiums skyrocketed, about thirty of Clark County's ninety-three obstetricians closed down their practices. Insurers, trying to reduce risk by limiting the remaining obstetricians to 125 deliveries a year, left thousands of pregnant women to hunt for doctors, some by desperately rifling through the Yellow Pages under "D." This year, the last pediatric cardiac surgery practice packed up and left the state.

Not surprisingly, Nevada was also unprepared for the anthrax crisis. Last October, when Microsoft's Reno office got suspicious powder in the mail that initially tested positive, an "outbreak of hysteria" ensued, said Matheis. The Clark County health district got 1,200 phone calls reporting everything from sugar to chalk dust, and investigated 500 of them with its skeletal staff. The state had no stockpiled antibiotics, and without a lab in Clark County, samples were shipped 500 miles north to Reno for testing.

The new federal money for bioterror preparedness, $10.5 million for Nevada alone, will help enormously. Of that, more than $2 million will go to building a public health laboratory in Las Vegas. But the money will do nothing to solve the problems of staff shortages and soaring medical malpractice premiums that forced the trauma center to close in July.

By July 4, the city of Las Vegas awoke to maximum fear of terror and a minimal medical system, with the trauma center closed for a second day. Governor Kenny Guinn had called an emergency session of the legislature and vowed to make sure that doctors did not abandon the state. An official at the nearby Nellis Air Force Base called the chief of orthopedics, Dr. Anthony Serfustini, asking what to do in the event of injuries. The lanky surgeon said that he reminded the man, You're the Air Force. You can fly your pilots to San Bernardino.

The community's medical infrastructure had declined to a level not seen in twenty-five years, said Dr. Fildes. And on July 4, the inevitable happened. Jim Lawson, 59, a grandfather of nine, was extracted from his mangled car and rushed to a nearby hospital—one with a nervous staff and little up-to-date trauma training—and died about an hour later. His daughter, Mary Rasar, said that she believes the trauma center, had it been open, could have saved him.

Atlanta's Health Emergency

On September 11, 2001, Dr. Arthur Kellerman was in Washington waiting to testify before Congress about the consequences of uninsurance when a plane struck the Pentagon, across the street from his hotel room. He immediately called back to Grady Memorial Hospital in Atlanta, where he oversees the emergency room residents, and got a disturbing report.

While Atlanta appeared to be safe from terrorism, the emergency room had twenty-five admitted patients waiting for hospital beds, the intensive-care area was packed and the staff had shut the emergency room to new patients. Worse, every emergency room in central Atlanta had declared saturation at the same time. None were taking new patients, and loaded ambulances were circling the block. If attacks had occurred in Atlanta that morning, "there was no way on God's earth we could have absorbed more patients," said Kellerman. Since then, all the Atlanta-area hospitals have gone on simultaneous diversion numerous times, leaving "nowhere to put casualties."

Despite all the effort to gear up for biological terror, the problem of overcrowded and understaffed emergency rooms—where terror's victims would be treated—has received only spotty attention. *U.S. News & World Report* featured the problem as a cover story, "Code Blue: Crisis in the E.R.," but it ran on September 10, 2001. A month after the attacks, Representative Henry Waxman prepared a report on ambulance diversions and their effect on disaster preparedness, finding a problem in thirty-two states. In at least nine states, every hospital in a local area had diverted ambulances simultaneously on a number of occasions, causing harm or even death to some patients. In Atlanta, one diverted patient was admitted only after he slipped into respiratory arrest while in the idling ambulance. The report quoted an editorial from the *St. Louis Post-Dispatch* last year:

> A word to the wise: Try not to get sick between 5 p.m. and midnight, when hospitals are most likely to go on diversion.

> Try not to get sick or injured at all in St. Louis or Kansas City,
> where diversions are most frequent. And if you're unlucky
> enough to end up in the back of an ambulance diverted from one
> E.R. to another, use the extra time to pray.

In Washington, Hauer has directed each region to identify 500
extra beds that can be "surged" or put into use quickly, which has
led a number of states to identify armories, school auditoriums, sta-
diums and hotels that can be used as MASH hospitals. But no bub-
ble tent can replace a hospital bed, with a full complement of
services readily available within the "golden hour" so crucial to
treating trauma patients, said Kellerman. And no proposal exists to
address the problem as a systemic one, in which a shortage of
nurses and cutbacks in reimbursement have made it impossible for
hospitals to staff enough beds.

Without a solution in sight, Grady Memorial uses a makeshift system, parking admitted patients on stretchers in the hallways
beneath handwritten numbers that run from 1 to 30. With the crisis
deepening, more numbers—1a, 1b, 1c, for example, seventeen additional spaces in all—have been squeezed between the initial numbers up and down the hall. The other night Kellerman had fifty
patients lined up waiting for rooms. "These are not disaster scenarios," he said. "This is Friday night. Wednesday afternoon."

September 11's Hard Lessons

New York City, with sixty-four hospitals, more than any other in
the country, was probably the best prepared for a mass-casualty
incident. Except that on September 11, most of the victims were
dead. Within minutes, the Bellevue emergency room was crowded
with hundreds of doctors, each bed with its own team of specialists,
from surgeons and psychiatrists to gynecologists. "The entire physi-
cian and nursing force of the hospital just came down at once," said
Dr. Brian Wexler, a third-year emergency medicine resident. At
Long Island College Hospital in Brooklyn, Dr. Lewis Kohl, chairman
of emergency medicine, said that by noon, he had a doctor and a
nurse for each available bed and could have tripled that number.
Doctors from all over the country at a defibrillation conference in
downtown Brooklyn were begging to work. "I spent most of the day
sending volunteers away," he recalled.

Tragically, so many people died that doctors had little to do. But
the people who answered phones, counseled the distraught or drew
blood from volunteers were overrun. A web-based patient locator
system cobbled together by the Greater New York Hospital Association got 2 million hits within days from frantic relatives. Beth Israel
Medical Center ran out of social workers, psychologists and psychiatrists to answer calls. "I answered the phone for half an hour and
said, 'I'm not qualified to do this,'" said Lisa Hogarty, vice president
of facility management for Continuum Health Partners, which runs
Beth Israel.

If anything, New York learned that targeted improvements, such as the creation of regional bioterror treatment centers, will not work. Susan Waltman, senior vice president of the Greater New York Hospital Association, told a CDC advisory committee in June that on September 11, 7,200 people, many covered in debris, wound up at 100 different hospitals, jumping on trains, boats and subways, or walking, to get away from downtown Manhattan. Now imagine if the debris had been tainted with some infectious biological agent. "You can't put the concentration of knowledge or staffing or supplies in regional centers," she said, "because you can't control where patients go."

The anthrax attacks, when they came, were a wake-up call of the worst kind. Baffled government officials with minimal scientific knowledge attributed the outbreak initially to farm visits, then contaminated water and finally to a fine, weaponized anthrax that had been sent through the mail. With no clear chain of communication or command for testing the samples, reporting the results, advising the medical community or informing the public, samples

---

"We were too focused on getting the public health job done, and we were not proactive in getting our message out."—Dr. David Fleming, CDC deputy director

---

vanished into dozens of laboratories. Conference calls between officials from different local, state and federal agencies were required to track them down, said those involved with the investigation. Testing methods were not standardized, with the Environmental Protection Agency, the postal service, the CDC, the FBI and the Defense Department all swabbing desktops and mailrooms using different methods and different kits, some of which had never been evaluated before. "A lot of those specimens that were said to be positive were not," said Dr. Philip Brachman, an anthrax expert and professor at the Rollins School of Public Health at Emory University.

For three weeks, from the initial outbreak on October 4, 2001, Americans seeking clear information from the CDC were out of luck. Until October 20, the agency's website still featured diabetes awareness month instead of the anthrax attacks. Dr. David Fleming, the CDC's deputy director for science and public health, said that while the CDC did respond quickly and accurately, "we were too focused on getting the public health job done, and we were not proactive in getting our message out."

But it wasn't just the CDC. Few officials nationwide knew what to do. In New York, police were marching into the city's public health laboratory carrying furniture and computers they suspected of being tainted, recalled Dr. David Perlin, scientific director of the

Public Health Research Institute, an advanced microbiology center then located a few floors above the city lab. Since those terrible days, the CDC under new director Dr. Julie Gerberding has made a great effort to establish its leadership and develop emergency response systems. "We have the people, we have the plans and now we have the practice," Gerberding, a microbiologist and veteran of the anthrax investigation, declared this September 11. "We're building our knowledge and capacity every day to assure that CDC and our partners are ready to respond to any terrorist event."

After September 11, however, such confident talk rings a little hollow. This past September the CDC laid out a radical plan for vaccinating much of the country within a week in the event of a smallpox attack. Medical experts greeted the plan as unrealistic and almost impossible to execute, given that disasters inevitably depart from plans to address them. They are pressing for the prevaccination of critical healthcare workers, and a decision on this is soon to be announced.

Preparing for the Worst

Past a strip mall outside Washington, and down a nondescript road, the federal OER keeps a warehouse of equipment that can all but navigate the end of civilization. It has the world's most sophisticated portable morgue units, each one able to support numerous autopsies. Another pile of boxes unfolds to become a full operating theater that can support open-heart surgery, if need be.

All this equipment can function during "catastrophic infrastructure failure," said Gary Moore, deputy director of the agency. And all of it can be loaded onto a C-5 transport plane and flown anywhere in the world. The federal government has massive resources—twelve fifty-ton pallets of drugs called the National Pharmaceutical Stockpile, which can get anywhere in the country in seven to twelve hours. After the New York City laboratory became contaminated, the Defense Department flew in six tons of laboratory equipment and turned a two-person testing operation into ten laboratories with three evidence rooms, a command center and seventy-five lab technicians operating around the clock.

This monumental surge capacity is crucial to preparedness. So are supplies. Dr. Kohl at Long Island College Hospital, who describes himself as a "paranoid of very long standing," feels ready. He's got a padlocked room full of gas masks, Geiger counters and Tyvek suits of varying thicknesses, most purchased after the anthrax attacks. Pulling one off the shelf, he declared confidently, "You could put this on and hang out in a bucket of Sarin."

But none of this can replace the simple stuff: hospital beds, trained people, fax machines, an infrastructure adequate for everyday use. Indeed, as states slash their public health and medical budgets, the opposite may be happening: We are building high-tech defenses on an ever-weakening infrastructure. In Colorado, for example, Governor Bill Owens cut all state funding for local public health departments in part because the federal government was supplying new funds. Public health officials there suddenly have federal money to hire bioterror experts but not enough state money to keep their offices open. While the Larimer County health department got $100,000 in targeted federal money, it lost $700,000 in state funds and fifteen staff positions. A spokesman for Governor Owens did not return calls seeking comment. States across the country are making similar cuts, said Dr. Gursky of the ANSER Institute, their weakened staffs left to prepare for bioterror while everyday health threats continue unchecked.

From her office window, Dr. Ruth Berkelman, director of Emory's Center for Public Health Preparedness, can see the new, $193 million infectious-disease laboratory rising on the CDC's forty-six-acre campus. While the new laboratory and information systems are needed, she says, if we detect smallpox, it's going to be because some doctor in an emergency room gets worried and "picks up the telephone."

A New Base for Developing Chemical, Biological Defenses[4]

By Steve Vogel
The Washington Post, February 20, 2003

In a new laboratory nestled among 92 acres of wetlands and forest near Aberdeen Proving Ground in Maryland, research will soon be underway on ways to better protect military personnel and civilians against chemical or biological warfare.

The Battelle Eastern Region Technology Center, a $20 million, 78,000-square-foot facility with 16 chemical and biological laboratories and 200 employees, has been completed and is set to open with a ribbon-cutting next month.

Battelle, founded 70 years ago, is one of the largest nonprofit research and development firms in the world. In recent years, Battelle has helped develop the first fully functional automatic pathogen detectors and has provided technical support for destroying the military's chemical weapons stockpile, which includes a large stock of mustard gas stored at Aberdeen Proving Ground's Edgewood Area.

Among other work, the new lab at Aberdeen will research ways to improve the detection of chemical and biological weapons, according to C. Warren Mullins, vice president of business development for the facility.

Fear of chemical or biological attack has created a burgeoning market for Battelle's services in the District, Northern Virginia and suburban Maryland. Battelle already has inspected more than 100 buildings in the Washington area and made recommendations on how to better protect them against chemical or biological attack, Mullins said.

The company has a contract with the Defense Advanced Research Projects Agency (DARPA) in Arlington to develop the "building of the future," Mullins said.

Battelle has been involved in the development of a mobile early warning detection system now being used around the Washington area.

Called the Joint Biological Point Detection System Vehicle, the system has been put in vans that can move to different locations in the Washington area to monitor air for biological agents.

A new generation is being developed, and one mounted in a Humvee was on display outside the new Battelle laboratory during a recent press briefing. The system had been undergoing vibration testing at Aberdeen, riding in the Humvee on off-road trails at the sprawling base on the Chesapeake Bay.

Mullins said Battelle chose to put the new laboratory in Aberdeen in part because of its proximity to the chemical and biological defense work being done by the U.S. Army Soldier and Biological Chemical Command headquartered at Aberdeen Proving Ground.

"If you had to pick one spot on Earth where more of it's done, you'd have to say Edgewood and Aberdeen," Mullins said.

Work at the lab will include research with dangerous pathogens, possibly including anthrax. The facility includes a bio-safety level III laboratory certified to handle some dangerous organisms.

"To do the kind of work we're doing, you have to have a lot of protection for the environment and a lot of controls," Mullins said.

Much of the work at the laboratory will be classified, he added. Said Mullins, "Some of our clients don't want their names mentioned."

101st Airborne in Iraq (Source: www.militaryphotos.net*).*

IV. Nuclear and Radiological Weapons

Editor's Introduction

I n 1934 Enrico Fermi irradiated uranium with neutrons, unknowingly achieving the first nuclear fission. Eleven years later, on August 6, 1945, the United States dropped an atomic bomb on the Japanese city of Hiroshima, effectively destroying it and bringing an end to World War II. Since then, the world has lived in the shadow of the nuclear threat. With many powerful nations, including Russia and China, stockpiling nuclear weapons, as well as rogue terrorist groups acquiring them on the black market, it seems only a matter of time before the world again faces the harrowing devastation of a nuclear assault. Section IV of this book covers conventional nuclear weapons, as well as radiological devices that can be assembled from materials that are relatively easy to acquire.

John Fialka details just how obtainable dangerous radiological materials are in his article "U.N. Unit Warns on Nuclear Material." According to Fialka, a recent study by the European Union revealed that 30,000 used radiation devices are in storage and are "at risk of being lost." Fialka also looks at the threat from the perspective of prevention, outlining stringent detection methods at border crossings and ports of entry and the development of devices that can detect radioactive material even through a shield.

In "Micro-Nukes" James Gordon Prather considers the efficiency of nuclear deterrence, as well as the next phase of nuclear conflict. While intercontinental ballistic missiles still comprise the backbone of a nuclear strike, attention is now shifting to micro-nukes, or what Prather calls "bunker-killers"—smaller tactical weapons that can strike specific targets with low-yield radiation. The war on terror finds many enemy operatives scuttling through labyrinthine underground caves, and according to Prather, these weapons may be the best way to drive them out.

The broad scope of the nuclear threat is examined in Bill Keller's "Nuclear Nightmares." Keller looks at the danger from all angles, including the black-market sales of nuclear warheads, the grim reality of radiological attacks, and the so-called "conex bombs" (nuclear weapons shipped in cargo containers). Two thousand of these containers arrive in American ports every hour, and fewer than 2 percent are inspected. A bomb delivered in a container such as this could reach New York, San Francisco, or Chicago, its contents remaining unknown until it is too late. Keller also details the expertise that is needed to build a nuclear bomb, showing the reader just how much terrorists have to know in order to do so. In addition, Keller discusses the threats to America's nuclear power plants, as well as what steps are being taken to protect them.

U.N. Unit Warns on Nuclear Material[1]

By John J. Fialka
Wall Street Journal, June 26, 2002

Poor controls and weak regulations governing radioactive materials mean that more than 22,000 machines that use them are vulnerable to terrorist efforts to make a "dirty bomb," according the International Atomic Energy Agency.

The new study by the Vienna-based affiliate of the United Nations came out as U.N. nuclear experts said they failed to find a set of highly dangerous nuclear batteries orphaned in Georgia after the breakup of the Soviet Union. The loss highlighted the growing problem of missing nuclear material used to make dirty bombs.

The agency's study found that in more than 100 countries there are no minimum standards in place to control radiation sources. Even in industrial countries that have some controls, there are large amounts of "orphaned" or missing materials, says the agency. It lists radiotherapy units in hospitals, industrial radiography equipment and food irradiators as the most potent and troublesome sources.

Orphaned radioactive materials are a "widespread phenomenon" in the states of the former Soviet Union, the report said. It noted that a recent study by the European Union found 30,000 used radiation devices in storage and "at risk of being lost."

The batteries from Georgia, palm-size cannisters brimming with highly radioactive strontium-90, were once used as electric generators for communications systems that lie off the power grid. Six of the devices have been recovered, and the final two were the subject of an intensive 80-man search that was directed by an international team of experts, who fanned out over a 350-square-mile stretch of wilderness.

In the U.S., the Nuclear Regulatory Commission has reported that companies have lost about 1,500 radioactive sources since 1996 and more than half were never recovered.

A dirty bomb, or a "radiation dispersal device," uses conventional explosives to spread radioactive wastes over a large area. While immediate casualties are likely to be relatively low, there could be longer term cancer risks and property risks involved because the

---

resulting radioactive mess could take months or years to clean up.

The IAEA found that there are millions of radioactive sources in use around the world, but "only a small percentage" have dirty-bomb potential. "What is needed is cradle-to-grave control of powerful radioactive sources to protect them against terrorism or theft," said Mohamed ElBaradei, director general of the agency.

> *[The IAEA] has counted 263 incidents of theft of radioactive sources since 1993.*

Mark Gwozdecky, a spokesman for the agency, cautioned that much speculation in the press about the threat posed by dirty bombs has been "based on bad science and really alarmist."

Potential terrorists face formidable risks in trying to steal and handle dangerously radioactive material, and then face the added difficulty of making a bomb that effectively disperses the material over a large area. "Imagine taking a bowling ball and trying to break it up into tiny little bits," said Mr. Gwozdecky.

But the agency has counted 263 incidents of theft of radioactive sources since 1993, most of them involving "small time crooks in hope of profit," he said. The relatively new threat of suicide bombers, he added, means that more controls are necessary. "And we believe the number of cases we've recorded vastly underestimates the scale of the problem," he said.

Tom Ridge, director of President Bush's Office of Homeland Security, told a House Energy subcommittee here yesterday that one of the missions of his agency and the future Department of Homeland Defense will be to set standards for effective radioactivity detection equipment and to provide a "point of access" in government for industries that make them or want to use them.

"We can't dictate the kinds of equipment they must purchase," said Mr. Ridge. He said the government would set standards to make sure that detectors are effective and measure consistently.

K. David Nokes, an official of Sandia National Laboratories, told the panel that simple Geiger counters aren't effective because they detect many different types of radioactive materials, raising the prospect of many false alarms.

His laboratory, he said, has come up with a detector that can "zero in" on materials that may pose a threat at airports and international ports. The device, called a "Radiation Assessment Identification and Detection System," could be produced at less than $50,000 per unit and can identify a radioactive source even if its radiation is shielded, he said.

Micro-Nukes[2]

By James Gordon Prather
The American Spectator, November/December 2001

One Cold War "lesson learned" at the Pentagon was that in confrontations between two nation-states, nukes do have a deterrent effect. The nuke deterrent worked in the Gulf War, as well. We suspected that Saddam Hussein might have nukes and chembio weapons, and so we warned him that if he used any of them against us or our allies, we would retaliate with nukes. It turns out Saddam did have chembio weapons, which he could have used. He didn't, even after his armies in the field had been utterly destroyed, leaving Baghdad practically defenseless.

A Gulf War corollary for our nuclear warriors was that our existing stockpile did not then include the kind of weapon we would have needed if Saddam—hunkered down in his bunker—had in fact unleashed his chembio weapons. What we wanted then was the type of low-yield, earth-penetrating "micro-nuke" bunker-killer proposed by two Los Alamos National Lab scientists in a 1991 article in *Strategic Review* entitled "Countering the Threat of the Well-armed Tyrant: A Modest Proposal for Small Nuclear Weapons."

By 1992 the Bush-Quayle administration had already begun to dismantle thousands of obsolete Cold War nukes. But George Bush—with Dick Cheney presiding at the Pentagon—supposed that a new class of nukes might need to be developed for the battlefields of the post–Cold War era. So, he vigorously opposed the efforts of the disarmament crowd in Congress to sign-on to an indefinite "zero-threshold" nuke test ban.

The next year, however, Clinton and Gore came to Washington and set out to dismantle our entire nuclear stockpile—not just nukes that were obsolete or excess to our more modest, post–Cold War needs. Clinton also announced that we would abide by the Comprehensive Test Ban Treaty—irrespective of whether the Senate ever ratified it—and that we would never again design, build or test new nukes. Clinton got the Democrat-controlled Congress to enact a total prohibition against "research and development which could lead to the production by the United States of a low-yield nuclear weapon . . . a nuclear weapon that has a yield of less than five kilotons."

The Pentagon got around this prohibition by modifying an existing weapon, the Air Force's B-61 "dial-a-yield" gravity bomb. The lowest yield that could be dialed—essentially by disabling parts of the otherwise far more powerful weapon—was indeed less than five kilotons. Without actually modifying the warhead, the Pentagon turned the thin-shelled gravity bomb into an earth-penetrating projectile. Though hardly the "micro-nuke" envisioned by the Los Alamos scientists, this "bunker-killer"—designated the B-61 Mod 11—entered the stockpile in 1997, and the B-2 bomber was certified to be its delivery vehicle.

Last year, the Republican-controlled Congress effectively repealed the Clinton ban on "micro-nuke" research. The 2001 National Defense Authorization Act expressly authorized the Department of Energy—which provides nuclear warheads to the Pentagon—to assist the Pentagon in "options assessments for defeating hardened and deeply buried targets." Of course, even if Congress actually does authorize development of new "micro-nukes," it will be years before they can actually be ready for use. In the meantime, the only bunker-killer we have is the B-61 Mod 11.

George W. Bush has declared war on terrorism, and that war's battlefields will be here, at home, and in about fifty nation-states around the world, all harboring terrorists, knowingly or otherwise. In particular, Osama bin Laden may now be hunkered down in a bunker—as Saddam was a decade ago. And he is protected by the Taliban, still recognized as the official Afghan government by neighboring Pakistan.

So what? Well, we are not at war with Afghanistan and the world is a very different place in 2001 than it was in 1991. In particular, in 1991 no Islamic nation-state—Iraq included—had nukes. Now at least one—Pakistan—does. In answering India's nuke tests in 1998 with their own, Pakistan has once again demonstrated the deterrent effect of nukes on nation-states. But can the threat of nuke retaliation deter suicidal terrorists? Obviously not. You can't retaliate against terrorists who are already dead.

That leaves pre-emptive strikes—say, with the B-61. But, before we nuke bin Laden—as some pundits and warhawk Congressmen have urged—maybe we ought to take into account that we will also be nuking the nation-state of Afghanistan. Then consider that Pakistan's version of our CIA—the Directorate for Inter-Services Intelligence, a rogue elephant if ever there was one—not only installed and sustains the Taliban, but is also the custodian of the several dozen Islamic nukes in the Pakistani stockpile. Just a thought.

Nuclear Nightmares[3]

By Bill Keller
The New York Times Magazine, May 26, 2002

Not If But When

Everybody who spends much time thinking about nuclear terrorism can give you a scenario, something diabolical and, theoretically, doable. Michael A. Levi, a researcher at the Federation of American Scientists, imagines a homemade nuclear explosive device detonated inside a truck passing through one of the tunnels into Manhattan. The blast would crater portions of the New York skyline, barbecue thousands of people instantly, condemn thousands more to a horrible death from radiation sickness and—by virtue of being underground—would vaporize many tons of concrete and dirt and river water into an enduring cloud of lethal fallout. Vladimir Shikalov, a Russian nuclear physicist who helped clean up after the 1986 Chernobyl accident, envisioned for me an attack involving highly radioactive cesium-137 loaded into some kind of homemade spraying device, and a target that sounded particularly unsettling when proposed across a Moscow kitchen table—Disneyland. In this case, the human toll would be much less ghastly, but the panic that would result from contaminating the Magic Kingdom with a modest amount of cesium—Shikalov held up his teacup to illustrate how much—would probably shut the place down for good and constitute a staggering strike at Americans' sense of innocence. Shikalov, a nuclear enthusiast who thinks most people are ridiculously squeamish about radiation, added that personally he would still be happy to visit Disneyland after the terrorists struck, although he would pack his own food and drink and destroy his clothing afterward.

Another Russian, Dmitry Borisov, a former official of his country's atomic energy ministry, conjured a suicidal pilot. (Suicidal pilots, for obvious reasons, figure frequently in these fantasies.) In Borisov's scenario, the hijacker dive-bombs an Aeroflot jetliner into the Kurchatov Institute, an atomic research center in a gentrifying neighborhood of Moscow, which I had just visited the day before our conversation. The facility contains 26 nuclear reactors of various sizes and a huge accumulation of radioactive material. The effect would probably be measured more in property values than in body bags, but some people say the same about Chernobyl.

Maybe it is a way to tame a fearsome subject by Hollywoodizing it, or maybe it is a way to drive home the dreadful stakes in the arid-sounding business of nonproliferation, but in several weeks of talking to specialists here and in Russia about the threats an amateur evildoer might pose to the homeland, I found an unnerving abundance of such morbid creativity. I heard a physicist wonder whether a suicide bomber with a pacemaker would constitute an effective radiation weapon. (I'm a little ashamed to say I checked that one, and the answer is no, since pacemakers powered by plutonium have not been implanted for the past 20 years.) I have had people theorize about whether hijackers who took over a nuclear research laboratory could improvise an actual nuclear explosion on the spot. (Expert opinions differ, but it's very unlikely.) I've been instructed how to disperse plutonium into the ventilation system of an office building.

The realistic threats settle into two broad categories. The less likely but far more devastating is an actual nuclear explosion, a great hole blown in the heart of New York or Washington, followed

---

The means to inflict nuclear harm on America have been available to rogues for a long time.

---

by a toxic fog of radiation. This could be produced by a black-market nuclear warhead procured from an existing arsenal. Russia is the favorite hypothetical source, although Pakistan, which has a program built on shady middlemen and covert operations, should not be overlooked. Or the explosive could be a homemade device, lower in yield than a factory nuke but still creating great carnage.

The second category is a radiological attack, contaminating a public place with radioactive material by packing it with conventional explosives in a "dirty bomb," by dispersing it into the air or water or by sabotaging a nuclear facility. By comparison with the task of creating nuclear fission, some of these schemes would be almost childishly simple, although the consequences would be less horrifying: a panicky evacuation, a gradual increase in cancer rates, a staggeringly expensive cleanup, possibly the need to demolish whole neighborhoods. Al Qaeda has claimed to have access to dirty bombs, which is unverified but entirely plausible, given that the makings are easily gettable.

Nothing is really new about these perils. The means to inflict nuclear harm on America have been available to rogues for a long time. Serious studies of the threat of nuclear terror date back to the 1970's. American programs to keep Russian nuclear ingredients from falling into murderous hands—one of the subjects high on the agenda in President Bush's meetings in Moscow this weekend—were hatched soon after the Soviet Union disintegrated a decade ago. When terrorists get around to trying their first nuclear assault, as you can be sure they will, there will be plenty of people entitled to say I told you so.

All September 11 did was turn a theoretical possibility into a felt danger. All it did was supply a credible cast of characters who hate us so much they would thrill to the prospect of actually doing it— and, most important in rethinking the probabilities, would be happy to die in the effort. All it did was give our nightmares legs.

And of the many nightmares animated by the attacks, this is the one with pride of place in our experience and literature—and, we know from his own lips, in Osama bin Laden's aspirations. In February, Tom Ridge, the Bush administration's homeland security chief, visited *The Times* for a conversation, and at the end someone asked, given all the things he had to worry about—hijacked airliners, anthrax in the mail, smallpox, germs in crop-dusters—what did he worry about most? He cupped his hands prayerfully and pressed his fingertips to his lips. "Nuclear," he said simply.

My assignment here was to stare at that fear and inventory the possibilities. How afraid should we be, and what of, exactly? I'll tell you at the outset, this was not one of those exercises in which weighing the fears and assigning them probabilities laid them to rest. I'm not evacuating Manhattan, but neither am I sleeping quite as soundly. As I was writing this early one Saturday in April, the floor began to rumble and my desk lamp wobbled precariously. Although I grew up on the San Andreas Fault, the fact that New York was experiencing an earthquake was only my second thought.

The best reason for thinking it won't happen is that it hasn't happened yet, and that is terrible logic. The problem is not so much that we are not doing enough to prevent a terrorist from turning our atomic knowledge against us (although we are not). The problem is that there may be no such thing as "enough."

25,000 Warheads, and It Only Takes One

My few actual encounters with the Russian nuclear arsenal are all associated with Thomas Cochran. Cochran, a physicist with a Tennessee lilt and a sense of showmanship, is the director of nuclear issues for the Natural Resources Defense Council, which promotes environmental protection and arms control. In 1989, when glasnost was in flower, Cochran persuaded the Soviet Union to open some of its most secret nuclear venues to a roadshow of American scientists and congressmen and invited along a couple of reporters. We visited a Soviet missile cruiser bobbing in the Black Sea and drank vodka with physicists and engineers in the secret city where the Soviets first produced plutonium for weapons.

Not long ago Cochran took me cruising through the Russian nuclear stockpile again, this time digitally. The days of glasnost theatrics are past, and this is now the only way an outsider can get close to the places where Russians store and deploy their nuclear weapons. On his office computer in Washington, Cochran has installed a detailed United States military map of Russia and super-imposed upon it high-resolution satellite photographs. We spent part of a morning mouse-clicking from missile-launch site to subma-rine base, zooming in like voyeurs and contemplating the possibility that a terrorist could figure out how to steal a nuclear warhead from one of these places.

"Here are the bunkers," Cochran said, enlarging an area the size of a football stadium holding a half-dozen elongated igloos. We were hovering over a site called Zhukovka, in western Russia. We were pleased to see it did not look ripe for a hijacking.

"You see the bunkers are fenced, and then the whole thing is fenced again," Cochran said. "Just outside you can see barracks and a rifle range for the guards. These would be troops of the 12th Main Directorate. Some-body's not going to walk off the street and get a Russian weapon out of this particular storage area."

Nuclear terror begins with the theft of a nuclear weapon. Why build one when so many are lying around for the taking?

In the popular culture, nuclear terror begins with the theft of a nuclear weapon. Why build one when so many are lying around for the taking? And stealing tends to make better drama than engineering. Thus the stolen nuke has been a staple in the literature at least since 1961, when Ian Fleming published *Thunderball*, in which the malevolent Spectre (the Special Executive for Counterintelligence, Terrorism, Revenge and Extortion, a strictly mercenary and more technologically sophisti-cated precursor to Al Qaeda) pilfers a pair of atom bombs from a crashed NATO aircraft. In the movie ver-sion of Tom Clancy's thriller *The Sum of All Fears*, due in theaters this week, neo-Nazis get their hands on a mislaid Israeli nuke, and viewers will get to see Baltimore blasted to oblivion.

Eight countries are known to have nuclear weapons—the United States, Russia, China, Great Britain, France, India, Pakistan and Israel. David Albright, a nuclear-weapons expert and president of the Institute for Science and International Security, points out that Pakistan's program in particular was built almost entirely through black markets and industrial espionage, aimed at circumventing Western export controls. Defeating the discipline of nuclear nonpro-liferation is ingrained in the culture. Disaffected individuals in Pakistan (which, remember, was intimate with the Taliban) would have no trouble finding the illicit channels or the rationalization for diverting materials, expertise—even, conceivably, a warhead.

But the mall of horrors is Russia, because it currently maintains something like 15,000 of the world's (very roughly) 25,000 nuclear warheads, ranging in destructive power from about 500 kilotons, which could kill a million people, down to the one-kiloton land mines that would be enough to make much of Manhattan uninhabitable. Russia is a country with sloppy accounting, a disgruntled military, an audacious black market and indigenous terrorists.

There is anecdotal reason to worry. Gen. Igor Valynkin, commander of the 12th Main Directorate of the Russian Ministry of Defense, the Russian military sector in charge of all nuclear weapons outside the Navy, said recently that twice in the past year terrorist groups were caught casing Russian weapons-storage facilities. But it's hard to know how seriously to take this. When I made the rounds of nuclear experts in Russia earlier this year, many were skeptical of these near-miss anecdotes, saying the security forces tend to exaggerate such incidents to dramatize their own prowess (the culprits are always caught) and enhance their budgets. On the whole, Russian and American military experts sound not very alarmed about the vulnerability of Russia's nuclear warheads. They say Russia takes these weapons quite seriously, accounts for them rigorously and guards them carefully. There is no confirmed case of a warhead being lost. Strategic warheads, including the 4,000 or so that President Bush and President Vladimir Putin have agreed to retire from service, tend to be stored in hard-to-reach places, fenced and heavily guarded, and their whereabouts are not advertised. The people who guard them are better paid and more closely vetted than most Russian soldiers.

Russia takes [nuclear] weapons quite seriously, accounts for them rigorously and guards them carefully.

Eugene E. Habiger, the four-star general who was in charge of American strategic weapons until 1998 and then ran nuclear antiterror programs for the Energy Department, visited several Russian weapons facilities in 1996 and 1997. He may be the only American who has actually entered a Russian bunker and inspected a warhead *in situ*. Habiger said he found the overall level of security comparable to American sites, although the Russians depend more on people than on technology to protect their nukes.

The image of armed terrorist commandos storming a nuclear bunker is cinematic, but it's far more plausible to think of an inside job. No observer of the unraveling Russian military has much trouble imagining that a group of military officers, disenchanted by the humiliation of serving a spent superpower, embittered by the wretched conditions in which they spend much of their military lives or merely greedy, might find a way to divert a warhead to a terrorist for the right price. (The Chechen warlord Shamil Basayev, infamous for such ruthless exploits as taking an entire hospital hostage, once hinted that he had an opportunity to buy a nuclear warhead from the stockpile.) The anecdotal evidence of desperation in the military is plentiful and disquieting. Every year the Russian press provides stories like that of the 19-year-old sailor who went on a rampage aboard an Akula-class nuclear submarine, killing eight people and threatening to blow up the boat and its nuclear reactor; or the five soldiers at Russia's nuclear-weapons test site who killed a guard, took a hostage and tried to hijack an aircraft; or the officers who reportedly stole five assault helicopters, with their weapons pods, and tried to sell them to North Korea.

The Clinton administration found the danger of disgruntled nuclear caretakers worrisome enough that it considered building better housing for some officers in the nuclear rocket corps. Congress, noting that the United States does not build housing for its own officers, rejected the idea out of hand.

If a terrorist did get his hands on a nuclear warhead, he would still face the problem of setting it off. American warheads are rigged with multiple PALs ("permissive action links")—codes and self-disabling devices designed to frustrate an unauthorized person from triggering the explosion. General Habiger says that when he examined Russian strategic weapons he found the level of protection comparable to our own. "You'd have to literally break the weapon apart to get into the gut," he told me. "I would submit that a more likely scenario is that there'd be an attempt to get hold of a warhead and not explode the warhead but extract the plutonium or highly enriched uranium." In other words, it's easier to take the fuel and build an entire weapon from scratch than it is to make one of these things go off.

Then again, Habiger is not an expert in physics or weapons design. Then again, the Russians would seem to have no obvious reason for misleading him about something that important. Then again, how many times have computer hackers hacked their way into encrypted computers we were assured were impregnable? Then again, how many computer hackers does Al Qaeda have? This subject drives you in circles.

The most troublesome gap in the generally reassuring assessment of Russian weapons security is those tactical nuclear warheads—smaller, short-range weapons like torpedoes, depth charges, artillery shells, mines. Although their smaller size and greater number make them ideal candidates for theft, they have gotten far less attention simply because, unlike all of our long-range weapons, they happen not to be the subject of any formal treaty. The first President Bush reached an informal understanding with President Gorbachev and then with President Yeltsin that both sides would gather and destroy thousands of tactical nukes. But the agreement included no inventories of the stockpiles, no outside monitoring, no verification of any kind. It was one of those trust-me deals that, in the hindsight of September 11, amount to an enormous black hole in our security.

Did I say earlier there are about 15,000 Russian warheads? That number includes, alongside the scrupulously counted strategic warheads in bombers, missiles and submarines, the commonly used estimate of 8,000 tactical warheads. But that figure is at best an educated guess. Other educated guesses of the tactical nukes in

Russia go as low as 4,000 and as high as 30,000. We just don't know. We don't even know if the Russians know, since they are famous for doing things off the books. "They'll tell you they've never lost a weapon," said Kenneth Luongo, director of a private antiproliferation group called the Russian-American Nuclear Security Advisory Council. "The fact is, they don't know. And when you're talking about warhead counting, you don't want to miss even one."

And where are they? Some are stored in reinforced concrete bunkers like the one at Zhukovka. Others are deployed. (When the submarine Kursk sank with its 118 crewmen in August 2000, the Americans' immediate fear was for its nuclear armaments. The standard load out for a submarine of that class includes a couple of nuclear torpedoes and possibly some nuclear depth charges.) Still others are supposed to be in the process of being dismantled under terms of various formal and informal arms control agreements. Some are in transit. In short, we don't really know.

The other worrying thing about tactical nukes is that their

One of the more interesting facts about the atom bomb dropped on Hiroshima is that it had never been tested.

---

anti-use devices are believed to be less sophisticated, because the weapons were designed to be employed in the battlefield. Some of the older systems are thought to have no permissive action links at all, so that setting one off would be about as complicated as hot-wiring a car.

Efforts to learn more about the state of tactical stockpiles have been frustrated by reluctance on both sides to let visitors in. Viktor Mikhailov, who ran the Russian Ministry of Atomic Energy until 1998 with a famous scorn for America's nonproliferation concerns, still insists that the United States programs to protect Russian nuclear weapons and material mask a secret agenda of intelligence-gathering. Americans, in turn, sometimes balk at reciprocal access, on the grounds that we are the ones paying the bills for all these safety upgrades, said the former Senator Sam Nunn, co-author of the main American program for securing Russian nukes, called Nunn-Lugar.

"We have to decide if we want the Russians to be transparent— I'd call it cradle-to-grave transparency with nuclear material and inventories and so forth," Nunn told me. "Then we have to open up more ourselves. This is a big psychological breakthrough we're talking about here, both for them and for us."

The Garage Bomb

One of the more interesting facts about the atom bomb dropped on Hiroshima is that it had never been tested. All of those spectral images of nuclear coronas brightening the desert of New Mexico—those were to perfect the more complicated plutonium device that was dropped on Nagasaki. "Little Boy," the Hiroshima bomb, was a rudimentary gunlike device that shot one projectile of highly enriched uranium into another, creating a critical mass that exploded. The mechanics were so simple that few doubted it would work, so the first experiment was in the sky over Japan.

The closest thing to a consensus I heard among those who study nuclear terror was this: building a nuclear bomb is easier than you think, probably easier than stealing one. In the rejuvenated effort to prevent a terrorist from striking a nuclear blow, this is where most of the attention and money are focused.

A nuclear explosion of any kind "is not a sort of high-probability thing," said a White House official who follows the subject closely. "But getting your hands on enough fissile material to build an improvised nuclear device, to my mind, is the least improbable of them all, and particularly if that material is highly enriched uranium in metallic form. Then I'm really worried. That's the one."

To build a nuclear explosive you need material capable of explosive nuclear fission, you need expertise, you need some equipment, and you need a way to deliver it.

Delivering it to the target is, by most reckoning, the simplest part. People in the field generally scoff at the mythologized suitcase bomb; instead they talk of a "conex bomb," using the name of those shack-size steel containers that bring most cargo into the United States. Two thousand containers enter America every hour, on trucks and trains and especially on ships sailing into more than 300 American ports. Fewer than 2 percent are cracked open for inspection, and the great majority never pass through an X-ray machine. Containers delivered to upriver ports like St. Louis or Chicago pass many miles of potential targets before they even reach customs.

"How do you protect against that?" mused Habiger, the former chief of our nuclear arsenal. "You can't. That's scary. That's very, very scary. You set one of those off in Philadelphia, in New York City, San Francisco, Los Angeles, and you're going to kill tens of thousands of people, if not more." Habiger's view is "It's not a matter of if; it's a matter of *when*"—which may explain why he now lives in San Antonio.

The Homeland Security office has installed a plan to refocus inspections, making sure the 2 percent of containers that get inspected are those without a clear, verified itinerary. Detectors will be put into place at ports and other checkpoints. This is good, but it hardly represents an ironclad defense. The detection devices are a long way from being reliable. (Inconveniently, the most feared bomb component, uranium, is one of the hardest radioactive substances to detect because it does not emit a lot of radiation prior to fission.) The best way to stop nuclear terror, therefore, is to keep the weapons out of terrorist hands in the first place.

The basic know-how of atom-bomb-building is half a century old, and adequate recipes have cropped up in physics term papers and high school science projects. The simplest design entails taking a lump of highly enriched uranium, about the size of a cantaloupe, and firing it down a big gun barrel into a second lump. Theodore Taylor, the nuclear physicist who designed both the smallest and the largest American nuclear-fission warheads before becoming a remorseful opponent of all things nuclear, told me he recently looked up "atomic bomb" in the *World Book Encyclopedia* in the upstate New York nursing home where he now lives, and he found enough basic information to get a careful reader started. "It's accessible all over the place," he said. "I don't mean just the basic principles. The sizes, specifications, things that work."

Most of the people who talk about the ease of assembling a nuclear weapon, of course, have never actually built one. The most authoritative assessment I found was a paper, "Can Terrorists Build Nuclear Weapons?," written in 1986 by five experienced nuke-makers from the Los Alamos weapons laboratory. I was relieved to learn that fabricating a nuclear weapon is not something a lone madman—even a lone genius—is likely to pull off in his hobby room. The paper explained that it would require a team with knowledge of "the physical, chemical and metallurgical properties of the various materials to be used, as well as characteristics affecting their fabrication; neutronic properties; radiation effects, both nuclear and biological; technology concerning high explosives and/or chemical propellants; some hydrodynamics; electrical circuitry; and others." Many of these skills are more difficult to acquire than, say, the ability to aim a jumbo jet.

The best way to stop nuclear terror . . . is to keep the weapons out of terrorist hands in the first place.

The schemers would also need specialized equipment to form the uranium, which is usually in powdered form, into metal, to cast it and machine it to fit the device. That effort would entail months of preparation, increasing the risk of detection, and it would require elaborate safeguards to prevent a mishap that, as the paper dryly put it, would "bring the operation to a close."

Still, the experts concluded, the answer to the question posed in the title, while qualified, was "Yes, they can."

David Albright, who worked as a United Nations weapons inspector in Iraq, says Saddam Hussein's unsuccessful crash program to build a nuclear weapon in 1990 illustrates how a single bad decision can mean a huge setback. Iraq had extracted highly enriched uranium from research-reactor fuel and had, maybe, barely enough for a bomb. But the manager in charge of casting the metal was so afraid the stuff would spill or get contaminated that he decided to melt it in tiny batches. As a result, so much of the uranium was wasted that he ended up with too little for a bomb.

"You need good managers and organizational people to put the elements together," Albright said. "If you do a straight-line extrapolation, terrorists will all get nuclear weapons. But they make mistakes."

On the other hand, many experts underestimate the prospect of a do-it-yourself bomb because they are thinking too professionally. All of our experience with these weapons is that the people who make them (states, in other words) want them to be safe, reliable, predictable and efficient. Weapons for the American arsenal are designed to survive a trip around the globe in a missile, to be accident-proof, to produce a precisely specified blast.

But there are many corners you can cut if you are content with a big, ugly, inefficient device that would make a spectacular impres-

---

"As you get smarter, you realize you can get by with less. You can do it in facilities that look like barns, garages, with simple machine tools."—David Albright, a U.N. **weapons inspector**

---

sion. If your bomb doesn't need to fit in a suitcase (and why should it?) or to endure the stress of a missile launch; if you don't care whether the explosive power realizes its full potential; if you're willing to accept some risk that the thing might go off at the wrong time or might not go off at all, then the job of building it is immeasurably simplified.

"As you get smarter, you realize you can get by with less," Albright said. "You can do it in facilities that look like barns, garages, with simple machine tools. You can do it with 10 to 15 people, not all Ph.D.'s, but some engineers, technicians. Our judgment is that a gun-type device is well within the capability of a terrorist organization."

All the technological challenges are greatly simplified if terrorists are in league with a country—a place with an infrastructure. A state is much better suited to hire expertise (like dispirited scientists from decommissioned nuclear installations in the old Soviet Union) or to send its own scientists for M.I.T. degrees.

Thus Tom Cochran said his greatest fear is what you might call a bespoke nuke—terrorists stealing a quantity of weapons-grade uranium and taking it to Iraq or Iran or Libya, letting the scientists and engineers there fashion it into an elementary weapon and then taking it away for a delivery that would have no return address.

That leaves one big obstacle to the terrorist nuke-maker: the fissile material itself.

To be reasonably sure of a nuclear explosion, allowing for some material being lost in the manufacturing process, you need roughly 50 kilograms—110 pounds—of highly enriched uranium. (For a weapon, more than 90 percent of the material should consist of the very unstable uranium-235 isotope.) Tom Cochran, the master of visual aids, has 15 pounds of depleted uranium that he keeps in a Coke can; an eight-pack would be plenty to build a bomb.

The world is awash in the stuff. Frank von Hippel, a Princeton physicist and arms-control advocate, has calculated that between 1,300 and 2,100 metric tons of weapons-grade uranium exists—at the low end, enough for 26,000 rough-hewed bombs. The largest stockpile is in Russia, which Senator Joseph Biden calls "the candy store of candy stores."

Until a decade ago, Russian officials say, no one worried much about the safety of this material. Viktor Mikhailov, who ran the atomic energy ministry and now presides over an affiliated research institute, concedes there were glaring lapses.

"The safety of nuclear materials was always on our minds, but the focus was on intruders," he said. "The system had never taken account of the possibility that these carefully screened people in the nuclear sphere could themselves represent a danger. The system was not designed to prevent a danger from within."

Then came the collapse of the Soviet Union and, in the early 90's, a few frightening cases of nuclear materials popping up on the black market.

If you add up all the reported attempts to sell highly enriched uranium or plutonium, even including those that have the scent of security-agency hype and those where the material was of uncertain quality, the total amount of material still falls short of what a bomb-maker would need to construct a single explosive.

But Yuri G. Volodin, the chief of safeguards at Gosatomnadzor, the Russian nuclear regulatory agency, told me his inspectors still discover one or two instances of attempted theft a year, along with dozens of violations of the regulations for storing and securing nuclear material. And as he readily concedes: "These are the detected cases. We can't talk about the cases we don't know." Alexander Pikayev, a former aide to the Defense Committee of the Russian Duma, said: "The vast majority of installations now have fences. But you know Russians. If you walk along the perimeter, you can see a hole in the fence, because the employees want to come and go freely."

The bulk of American investment in nuclear safety goes to lock the stuff up at the source. That is clearly the right priority. Other programs are devoted to blending down the highly enriched uranium to a diluted product unsuitable for weapons but good as reactor fuel. The Nuclear Threat Initiative, financed by Ted Turner and led by Nunn, is studying ways to double the rate of this diluting process.

Still, after 10 years of American subsidies, only 41 percent of Russia's weapon-usable material has been secured, according to the United States Department of Energy. Russian officials said they can't even be sure how much exists, in part because the managers of nuclear facilities, like everyone else in the Soviet industrial complex, learned to cook their books. So the barn door is still pretty seriously ajar. We don't know whether any horses have gotten out.

> *Outside of Belgrade, in a research reactor at Vinca, sits sufficient material for a bomb.*

And it is not the only barn. William C. Potter, director of the Center for Nonproliferation Studies at the Monterey Institute of International Studies and an expert in nuclear security in the former Soviet states, said the American focus on Russia has neglected other locations that could be tempting targets for a terrorist seeking bomb-making material. There is, for example, a bomb's worth of weapons-grade uranium at a site in Belarus, a country with an erratic president and an anti-American orientation. There is enough weapons-grade uranium for a bomb or two in Kharkiv, in Ukraine. Outside of Belgrade, in a research reactor at Vinca, sits sufficient material for a bomb—and there it sat while NATO was bombarding the area.

"We need to avoid the notion that because the most material is in Russia, that's where we should direct all of our effort," Potter said. "It's like assuming the bank robber will target Fort Knox because that's where the most gold is. The bank robber goes where the gold is most accessible."

Weapons of Mass Disruption

The first and, so far, only consummated act of nuclear terrorism took place in Moscow in 1995, and it was scarcely memorable. Chechen rebels obtained a canister of cesium, possibly from a hospital they had commandeered a few months before. They hid it in a Moscow park famed for its weekend flea market and called the press. No one was hurt. Authorities treated the incident discreetly, and a surge of panic quickly passed.

The story came up in virtually every conversation I had in Russia about nuclear terror, usually to illustrate that even without splitting atoms and making mushroom clouds a terrorist could use radioactivity—and the fear of it—as a potent weapon.

The idea that you could make a fantastic weapon out of radioactive material without actually producing a nuclear bang has been around since the infancy of nuclear weaponry. During World War II, American scientists in the Manhattan Project worried that the Germans would rain radioactive material on our troops storming the beaches on D-Day. Robert S. Norris, the biographer of the Manhattan Project director, Gen. Leslie R. Groves, told me that the United States took this threat seriously enough to outfit some of the D-Day soldiers with Geiger counters.

No country today includes radiological weapons in its armories. But radiation's limitations as a military tool—its tendency to drift afield with unplanned consequences, its long-term rather than short-term lethality—would not necessarily count against it in the mind of a terrorist. If your aim is to instill fear, radiation is anthrax-plus. And unlike the fabrication of a nuclear explosive, this is terror within the means of a soloist.

That is why, if you polled the universe of people paid to worry about weapons of mass destruction (W.M.D., in the jargon), you would find a general agreement that this is probably the first thing we'll see. "If there is a W.M.D. attack in the next year, it's likely to be a radiological attack," said Rose Gottemoeller, who handled Russian nuclear safety in the Clinton administration and now follows the subject for the Carnegie Endowment. The radioactive heart of a dirty bomb could be spent fuel from a nuclear reactor or isotopes separated out in the process of refining nuclear fuel. These materials are many times more abundant and much, much less protected than the high-grade stuff suitable for bombs. Since September 11, Russian officials have begun lobbying hard to expand the program of American aid to include protection of these lower-grade materials, and the Bush administration has earmarked a few million dollars to study the problem. But the fact is that radioactive material suitable for terrorist attacks is so widely available that there is little hope of controlling it all.

The guts of a dirty bomb could be cobalt-60, which is readily available in hospitals for use in radiation therapy and in food processing to kill the bacteria in fruits and vegetables. It could be cesium-137, commonly used in medical gauges and radiotherapy machines. It could be americium, an isotope that behaves a lot like plutonium and is used in smoke detectors and in oil prospecting. It could be plutonium, which exists in many research laboratories in America. If you trust the security of those American labs, pause and reflect that the investigation into the great anthrax scare seems to be focused on disaffected American scientists.

Back in 1974, Theodore Taylor and Mason Willrich, in a book on the dangers of nuclear theft, examined things a terrorist might do if he got his hands on 100 grams of plutonium—a thimble-size amount. They calculated that a killer who dissolved it, made an aerosol and introduced it into the ventilation system of an office building could deliver a lethal dose to the entire floor area of a large skyscraper. But plutonium dispersed outdoors in the open air, they estimated, would be far less effective. It would blow away in a gentle wind.

The Federation of American Scientists recently mapped out for a Congressional hearing the consequences of various homemade dirty bombs detonated in New York or Washington. For example, a bomb made with a single footlong pencil of cobalt from a food irradiation plant and just 10 pounds of TNT and detonated at Union Square in a light wind would send a plume of radiation drifting across three states. Much of Manhattan would be as contaminated as the permanently closed area around the Chernobyl nuclear plant. Anyone living in Manhattan would have at least a 1-in-100 chance of dying from cancer caused by the radiation. An area reaching deep into the Hudson Valley would, under current Environmental Protection Agency standards, have to be decontaminated or destroyed.

Frank von Hippel, the Princeton physicist, has reviewed the data, and he pointed out that this is a bit less alarming than it sounds. "Your probability of dying of cancer in your lifetime is already about 20 percent," he said. "This would increase it to 20.1 percent. Would you abandon a city for that? I doubt it."

Indeed, some large portion of our fear of radiation is irrational. And yet the fact that it's all in your mind is little consolation if it's

> *There are measures the government can take to diminish the dangers of a radiological weapon, and many of them are getting more serious consideration.*

also in the minds of a large, panicky population. If the actual effect of a radiation bomb is that people clog the bridges out of town, swarm the hospitals and refuse to return to live and work in a contaminated place, then the impact is a good deal more than psychological. To this day, there is bitter debate about the actual health toll from the Chernobyl nuclear accident. There are researchers who claim that the people who evacuated are actually in worse health overall from the trauma of relocation than those who stayed put and marinated in the residual radiation. But the fact is, large swaths of developed land around the Chernobyl site still lie abandoned, much of it bulldozed down to the subsoil. The Hart Senate Office Building was closed for three months by what was, in hindsight, our society's inclination to err on the side of alarm.

There are measures the government can take to diminish the dangers of a radiological weapon, and many of them are getting more serious consideration. The Bush administration has taken a lively new interest in radiation-detection devices that might catch dirty-bomb materials in transit. A White House official told me the administration's judgment is that protecting the raw materials of radiological terror is worth doing, but not at the expense of more catastrophic threats.

"It's all over," he said. "It's not a winning proposition to say you can just lock all that up. And then, a bomb is pretty darn easy to make. You don't have to be a rocket scientist to figure about fertilizer and diesel fuel." A big fertilizer bomb of the type Timothy McVeigh used to kill 168 people in Oklahoma City, spiced with a dose of cobalt or cesium, would not tax the skills of a determined terrorist.

"It's likely to happen, I think, in our lifetime," the official said. "And it'll be like Oklahoma City plus the Hart Office Building. Which is real bad, but it ain't the World Trade Center."

The Peril of Power Plants

Every eight years or so the security guards at each of the country's 103 nuclear power stations and at national weapons labs can expect to be attacked by federal agents armed with laser-tag rifles. These mock terror exercises are played according to elaborate rules, called the "design basis threat," that in the view of skeptics favor the defense. The attack teams can include no more than three commandos. The largest vehicle they are permitted is an S.U.V. They are allowed to have an accomplice inside the plant, but only one. They are not allowed to improvise. (The mock assailants at one Department of Energy lab were ruled out of order because they commandeered a wheelbarrow to cart off a load of dummy plutonium.) The mock attacks are actually announced in advance. Even playing by these rules, the attackers manage with some regularity to penetrate to the heart of a nuclear plant and damage the core. Representative Edward J. Markey, a Massachusetts Democrat and something of a scourge of the nuclear power industry, has recently identified a number of shortcomings in the safeguards, including, apparently, lax standards for clearing workers hired at power plants.

One of the most glaring lapses, which nuclear regulators concede and have promised to fix, is that the design basis threat does not contemplate the possibility of a hijacker commandeering an airplane and diving it into a reactor. In fact, the protections currently in place don't consider the possibility that the terrorist might be willing, even eager, to die in the act. The government assumes the culprits would be caught while trying to get away.

A nuclear power plant is essentially a great inferno of decaying radioactive material, kept under control by coolant. Turning this device into a terrorist weapon would require cutting off the coolant so the atomic furnace rages out of control and, equally important, getting the radioactive matter to disperse by an explosion or fire. (At Three Mile Island, the coolant was cut off and the reactor core melted down, generating vast quantities of radiation. But the thick walls of the containment building kept the contaminant from being released, so no one died.)

One way to accomplish both goals might be to fly a large jetliner into the fortified building that holds the reactor. Some experts say a jet engine would stand a good chance of bursting the containment vessel, and the sheer force of the crash might disable the cooling system—rupturing the pipes and cutting off electricity that pumps the water through the core. Before nearby residents had begun to evacuate, you could have a meltdown that would spew a volcano of radioactive isotopes into the air, causing fatal radiation sickness for those exposed to high doses and raising lifetime cancer rates for miles around.

This sort of attack is not as easy, by a long shot, as hitting the World Trade Center. The reactor is a small, low-lying target, often nestled near the conspicuous cooling towers, which could be destroyed without great harm. The reactor is encased in reinforced concrete several feet thick, probably enough, the industry contends, to withstand a crash. The pilot would have to be quite a marksman, and somewhat lucky. A high wind would disperse the fumes before they did great damage.

Invading a plant to produce a meltdown, even given the record of those mock attacks, would be more complicated, because law enforcement from many miles around would be on the place quickly, and because breaching the containment vessel is harder from within. Either invaders or a kamikaze attacker could instead target the more poorly protected cooling ponds, where used plutonium sits, encased in great rods of zirconium alloy. This kind of sabotage would take longer to generate radiation and would be far less lethal.

Discussion of this kind of potential radiological terrorism is colored by passionate disagreements over nuclear power itself. Thus the nuclear industry and its rather tame regulators sometimes sound dismissive about the vulnerability of the plants (although less so since Sept. 11), while those who regard nuclear power as inherently evil tend to overstate the risks. It is hard to sort fact from fear-mongering.

Nuclear regulators and the industry grumpily concede that Sept. 11 requires a new estimate of their defenses, and under prodding from Congress they are redrafting the so-called design basis threat, the one plants are required to defend against. A few members of Congress have proposed installing ground-to-air missiles at nuclear plants, which most experts think is a recipe for a disastrous mishap.

"Probably the only way to protect against someone flying an aircraft into a nuclear power plant," said Steve Fetter of the University of Maryland, "is to keep hijackers out of cockpits."

Being Afraid

For those who were absorbed by the subject of nuclear terror before it became fashionable, the months since the terror attacks have been, paradoxically, a time of vindication. President Bush, whose first budget cut $100 million from the programs to protect Russian weapons and material (never a popular program among conservative Republicans), has become a convert. The administration has made nuclear terror a priority, and it is getting plenty of goading to keep it one. You can argue with their priorities and their budgets, but it's hard to accuse anyone of indifference. And resistance—from scientists who don't want security measures to impede their access to nuclear research materials, from generals and counterintelligence officials uneasy about having their bunkers inspected, from nuclear regulators who worry about the cost of nuclear power, from conservatives who don't want to subsidize the Russians to do much of anything—has become harder to sustain. Intelligence gathering on nuclear material has been abysmal, but it is now being upgraded; it is a hot topic at meetings between American and foreign intelligence services, and we can expect more numerous and more sophisticated sting operations aimed at disrupting the black market for nuclear materials. Putin, too, has taken notice. Just before leaving to meet Bush in Crawford, Tex., in November, he summoned the head of the atomic energy ministry to the Kremlin on a Saturday to discuss nuclear security. The subject is now on the regular agenda when Bush and Putin talk.

These efforts can reduce the danger but they cannot neutralize the fear, particularly after we have been so vividly reminded of the hostility some of the world feels for us, and of our vulnerability.

Fear is personal. My own—in part, because it's the one I grew up with, the one that made me shiver through the Cuban missile crisis and *On the Beach*—is the horrible magic of nuclear fission. A dirty bomb or an assault on a nuclear power station, ghastly as that would be, feels to me within the range of what we have survived. As the White House official I spoke with said, it's basically Oklahoma City plus the Hart Office Building. A nuclear explosion is in a different realm of fears and would test the country in ways we can scarcely imagine.

As I neared the end of this assignment, I asked Matthew McKinzie, a staff scientist at the Natural Resources Defense Council, to run a computer model of a one-kiloton nuclear explosion in Times Square, half a block from my office, on a nice spring workday. By the standards of serious nuclear weaponry, one kiloton is a junk bomb, hardly worthy of respect, a fifteenth the power of the bomb over Hiroshima.

A couple of days later he e-mailed me the results, which I combined with estimates of office workers and tourist traffic in the area. The blast and searing heat would gut buildings for a block in every direction, incinerating pedestrians and crushing people at their desks. Let's say 20,000 dead in a matter of seconds. Beyond this, to a distance of more than a quarter mile, anyone directly exposed to the fireball would die a gruesome death from radiation sickness within a day—anyone, that is, who survived the third-degree burns. This larger circle would be populated by about a quarter million people on a workday. Half a mile from the explosion, up at Rockefeller Center and down at Macy's, unshielded onlookers would expect a slower death from radiation. A mushroom cloud of irradiated debris would blossom more than two miles into the air, and then, 40 minutes later, highly lethal fallout would begin drifting back to earth, showering injured survivors and dooming rescue workers. The poison would ride for 5 or 10 miles on the prevailing winds, deep into the Bronx or Queens or New Jersey.

A terrorist who pulls off even such a small-bore nuclear explosion will take us to a whole different territory of dread from Sept. 11. It is the event that preoccupies those who think about this for a living, a category I seem to have joined.

"I think they're going to try," said the physicist David Albright. "I'm an optimist at heart. I think we can catch them in time. If one goes off, I think we will survive. But we won't be the same. It will affect us in a fundamental way. And not for the better."

V. Non-lethal Weapons

Editor's Introduction

To many people, the use of non-lethal weapons is the next step in the evolution of modern warfare. Waging war with almost no fatalities or collateral damage seems almost too good to be true, and in fact, at this point in time, it may well be. In October 2002 Chechen rebels seized control of a Moscow theater. In the hope of flushing them out, Russian security officials flooded the theater with an opiate gas intended to incapacitate the hostage takers and clear the way for rescue forces. Instead, over 100 hostages, as well as their captors, died from the gas. This incident is just one of many examples cited in the ever-growing debate over the use of non-lethal weapons. Section V looks at that debate, as well as the very real purposes of these weapons, which are today being employed on battlefields around the globe.

Brad Knickerbocker's "Bang! You're Incapacitated" explains how several non-lethal weapons actually work. He describes electromagnetic pulse weapons that knock out power lines and communication devices, low-frequency acoustical weapons that can cause an enemy to become disoriented or even to vomit perniciously, and so-called "sticky foam," which can bog down an infantry or cause a tank to slide off its path. Knickerbocker also considers the use of non-lethal weapons pragmatically, explaining how the advent of these devices does not yet mean an end to conventional warfare.

Bill Mesler's article "The Pentagon's 'Non-lethal' Gas" looks at the Moscow debacle in light of the persistent clash over non-lethal weapons. Mesler also explains the history of non-lethal weapons and their place in modern theaters of war. He briefly describes the 1993 battle of Mogadishu, a pitched struggle in which U.S. special forces had a difficult time distinguishing combatants from non-combatants. Such a situation, some argue, is exactly why the military should use non-lethal tools, such as rubber bullets.

In "U.S. Troops to Find New Uses for Non-lethal Weaponry," Harold Kennedy shows how soldiers are already learning to apply non-lethal tactics in combat. Kennedy describes a course being offered to marines at Fort Leonard Wood in Montana which teaches the basics of unarmed self-defense, crowd-control tactics, and the use of weapons such as the pulsed-energy projectile, which delivers a stunning electrical charge not unlike the phasers on *Star Trek*.

Bang! You're Incapacitated[1]

By Brad Knickerbocker
The Christian Science Monitor, December 12, 2002

Imagine a war where hardly anybody gets killed.

Not a giant game of paintball or capture-the-flag, exactly, but a conflict where the most crucial weapons make an opponent simply faint or throw up or fall down with leg cramps—unable to fight back but not seriously harmed, and willing, if not eager, to surrender. Or a battlefield where enemy tanks slide around harmlessly like bumper cars at a carnival, where an opposing force's electronic gear gets zapped and conks out without having to be blown up.

Sound far out? A mad scientist's dream? A peace advocate's fantasy?

As the United States fights a war on terrorism and prepares for possible war with Iraq, development and advocacy of nonlethal weapons are accelerating. Major defense contractors are involved. Military professionals trained to be able to kill people and destroy things are seeing the benefits. The government-sponsored National Research Council recently urged the military services to give greater priority to such devices.

"Nonlethal weapons are an additional way to provide greater security for military bases and protect our forces," says Miriam John, who chaired the committee of experts that wrote the NRC report.

The interest is being driven by two things: changes in fighting methods to match a new set of military challenges including terrorism, involvement in other nations' civil wars, and military presence in countries that have descended into anarchy; and steady advances in technology.

Among the new kinds of weapons being researched and in some cases developed:

- High-powered "active denial" microwave systems that can inflict intense pain for brief periods without killing or gravely injuring the person. With a range of several hundred yards, they could fend off crowds of rock throwers (or pick out a single sniper among civilians) without resorting to deadly force.

- Electromagnetic pulse weapons that foul up radars, radios, computers, navigational devices, and other equipment by destroying semiconductors.

- Materials such as "sticky foam" to bog down soldiers or equipment and special lubricants to send enemy vehicles spinning. These are called "stick-ems" and "slick-ems."

- Biological agents that can "eat" oil, plastics, and other material essential to an enemy's gear. The idea here is to pattern the "bugs" now used to help clean up oil spills. As one advocate says, "Organisms don't care whether it's an oil slick on the ocean or a national oil supply."

- Calmatives—gases that can temporarily incapacitate a squad of soldiers, terrorists holed up with hostages, or an angry crowd.

- Malodorants—chemicals that mimic the most revolting smells (rotting food or human waste) and can disperse attackers like a skunk at a garden party.

- Low-frequency acoustical weapons that can nauseate or disorient people.

- Barrier and entanglement devices, such as might have prevented the small boat loaded with explosives from severely damaging the destroyer USS Cole in Yemen two years ago.

"Nonlethals fill the gap between the breakdown of diplomacy and the full-scale use of conventional weapons," says Capt. Shawn Turner of the Joint Non-Lethal Weapons Directorate, which is run by the Marine Corps.

So far, the US Defense Department is spending only tens of millions of dollars a year on such technology—pocket lint to the Pentagon. But with an eye to future military conflicts, laboratories and major defense contractors are investing far more. And while the nation's professional warriors were once quite dubious about nonlethal weapons (just as they had grumbled over peacekeeping missions), they now acknowledge a world of terrorism and failed states where much of their work will involve civilian settings and a heightened need to keep casualties to a minimum.

No one predicts an end to machine guns and hand grenades, tanks and bombers.

"Nonlethal weapons are about pragmatic application of force, not a peace movement," says John Alexander, a retired Army colonel and former head of nonlethal defense programs at Los Alamos National Laboratory.

But the idea is to keep that application of force at a lower level than typically is the case when the shooting starts.

Non-lethal Technologies

Conductive Particles—Particles that can induce short circuits in electrical or electronic equipment.

Depolymerizing Agents—Chemicals that cause polymers to dissolve or decompose.

Liquid-Metal Embrittlement Agents—Agents that change the molecular structure of base metals or alloys, significantly reducing their strength.

Nonnuclear Electromagnetic Pulse—Pulse generators producing gigawatts of power that could be used to explode ammunition dumps or paralyze electronic systems.

High-Powered Microwave—Generators that produce microwave pulses similar to electromagnetic pulses. Microwave frequencies may have antipersonnel applications that can cause pain or incapacitation.

Pol Contaminators—Additives that cause fuel to jell or solidify, making it unusable.

Supercaustic—Acids that corrode or degrade structural materials.

Super Lubricants—Substances that cause lack of traction.

Acoustics—Very-low-frequency sound generators that could be tuned to incapacitate people.

Foam—Sticky or space-filling material that can impede mobility or deny access to equipment.

Isotropic Radiators—Conventional weapons that produce a flash that can dazzle people or optical sensors.

Lasers—Low-energy lasers that temporarily blind people or disable optical or infrared systems.

Calmative Agents—Chemical substances designed to temporarily incapacitate people.

Source: "Non-Lethal Technologies: Implications for Military Strategy," by Joseph Siniscalchi, Colonel, USAF © Copyright 2002. *The Christian Science Monitor*

"A nonlethal weapon has to produce an effect on a target that is both short-term and reversible," says Dr. John, a chemical engineer with the Sandia National Laboratories who chaired the NRC study.

Weapons designed to be less than lethal have been around for years: rubber bullets, water cannons, tear gas. Mostly, they've been used by police forces rather than the military.

But especially since the end of the cold war, when US military forces found themselves spending much time trying to keep the peace in dangerous places like Somalia, Bosnia, and Haiti, nonlethal weapons have made more sense for them as well.

Foreseen on the immediate horizon are what defense experts call "Military Operations on Urbanized Terrain" (MOUT)—violent street fighting, in plain language. Retired Gen. Charles Krulak, former commandant of the Marine Corps, calls this "the three-block war."

"In one moment in time, our service members will be feeding and clothing displaced refugees—providing humanitarian assistance," he says. "In the next moment, they will be holding two warring tribes apart—conducting peacekeeping operations. Finally, they will be fighting a highly lethal mid-intensity battle. All within three city blocks."

Colonel Alexander, author of *Future War: Non-Lethal Weapons in Twenty-First-Century Warfare*, sees the same scenario being played out in terrorist events. "We're going to end up having to combat terrorist cells in major metropolitan areas, and one of the things we're going to have to do is discriminate between combatants and noncombatants," he says.

Opponents see several major problems with nonlethal weapons.

Foreseen on the immediate horizon are what defense experts call "Military Operations on Urbanized Terrain."

"Within the framework of law and with independent oversight, I have no problem in principle with nonlethal weapons," says Steven Aftergood, who heads a project on government secrecy for the Federation of American Scientists. "Unfortunately, there is reason to question whether either of these conditions is being met today."

"Parts of the program—which includes a diverse array of technologies—seem to be on auto-pilot and utterly without public accountability," says Mr. Aftergood. "Likewise, it seems questionable whether all of the chemical and biological nonlethal weapons programs are formally compliant with the Chemical Weapons Convention or the Biological Weapons Convention."

To some humanitarian organizations, such weaponry is associated with repressive regimes.

Regarding electroshock stun weapons, Amnesty International reports: "This is a fast-growing industry, whose products are often not properly tested and many of whose clients are well known to have used the products to routinely and systematically torture men, women and children. . . . Yet many governments—including the USA, which is the largest producing country—allow this trade."

One might think that humanitarian groups would favor non-lethal weapons in war if these would ultimately leave fewer people maimed, killed, and displaced. But they don't agree that fewer casualties result. In fact, many argue that such weapons lower the threshold for initial aggression, eventually leading to more suffering.

Critics of the recent National Research Council study on nonlethal weapons are especially concerned about starting a new arms race in chemical and biological weapons.

The report, says University of California microbiologist Mark Wheelis, "contains a number of serious errors of law and science that lead it to irresponsible and dangerous recommendations."

In response, supporters of nonlethal weapons say decades-old treaties concerning chemical and biological weapons are virtually unenforceable, and that the authors never envisioned a time when such substances could be designed to prevent loss of life.

"Would you accept speed limits based on technology that's 100 years old?" asks Alexander.

It seems likely, in any case, that research and development in the field will accelerate, with perhaps profound results for warfare and war prevention.

Writing in the *Naval War College Review*, Army National Guard Lt. Col. Margaret-Anne Coppernoll predicts that "the introduction of nonlethal weapons on the battlefield will be as significant as the introduction of gunpowder during the European Renaissance."

The technology may be "Star Wars" and the new battlefield set in a civilian scene. But the idea is more than 2,000 years old. In the 4th century BC, Chinese military strategist Sun Tzu put it this way: "Hence to fight and conquer in all your battles is not supreme excellence; supreme excellence consists in breaking the enemy's resistance without fighting."

The Pentagon's "Non-lethal" Gas[2]

By Bill Mesler
The Nation, February 11, 2003

When Chechen rebels seized more than 700 hostages in a Moscow theater last October, Russian security officials must have believed they had come up with the perfect solution: They would put them to sleep. An opiate gas would be piped into the theater, clearing the way for commandos to enter, disarm the hijackers and rescue the civilians. In the end, 117 people were killed—not by the hostage-takers but by the chemical agent used by their rescuers.

In recent years, the US military has become infatuated with a variety of "incapacitating" chemical weapons, including fentanyl, the opiate believed to have been used by Russian forces. And while the use of incapacitants in Russia might have been legal under international law because it was a police action, the Pentagon's development of what the military calls "nonlethal calmatives" appears to violate chemical weapons treaties prohibiting the military use of such agents.

Capable of taking out enemy soldiers without killing them, calmatives were once seen as ideal from a public relations standpoint. But some planners also recognized their inherent dangers: Any enemy attacked by such weapons—deadly or not—is sure to respond with whatever biological or chemical weapons it has. The detractors' view eventually prevailed, and "incapacitating agents" were barred by an executive order signed by Richard Nixon in 1969. In 1972, the ban was solidified into international law when the United States signed the Biological and Toxin Weapons Convention (BTWC), which for the past three decades has been the cornerstone of international efforts to stop the spread of nonnuclear weapons of mass destruction. The Chemical Weapons Convention (CWC), signed in 1993 by President Clinton, went even further by banning the military use of such riot-control agents as tear gas.

But in recent years, the Pentagon has gradually turned to new and dangerously loose interpretations of international treaties that would allow the military use of incapacitating chemicals. The changes in policy amount to a "very serious assault" on the CWC, warns University of California, Davis, microbiology professor Mark Wheelis, who has written extensively on chemical and biological weapons issues. "And it is being guided by very narrow, short-sighted tactical concerns. If the United States is allowed to continue to develop [calmatives] sooner or later we are going to be employing

---

2. Reprinted with permission from the February 17, 2003, issue of *The Nation*.

artillery shells and aerial bombs [loaded with calmatives]. And we are going to have troops trained to use them. If the United States does this, other countries will follow suit. The long-term implications are quite profound." According to Wheelis, it amounts to no less than "preparing for chemical war."

The military's current fixation with incapacitating chemicals dates back to the 1993 debacle in Somalia, when US troops battled Somalian paramilitaries in the streets and suburbs of Mogadishu. The problems created by the ambiguous military situation—when it was often difficult to distinguish between combatants and non-combatants—eventually led the Defense Department to create the Joint Non-Lethal Weapons Directorate (JNLWD) in 1997 to study alternative weapons for low-intensity conflicts.

Many of the new weapons the JNLWD has developed, like rubber bullets and twelve-gauge beanbag shotguns, seem legal and relatively innocuous by international standards. But it has also explored a variety of divergent psychoactive drugs—Prozac, Valium and Zoloft, to name a few—that have the effect of making

---

Among drugs that seem to hold promise for military use are fentanyl and the anesthetic ketamine—sold illegally as "Special K."

---

it harder for enemy soldiers to fight in combat. Among drugs that seem to hold promise for military use are fentanyl and the anesthetic ketamine—sold illegally as "Special K," a psychedelic similar to PCP—which, in theory, can put people to sleep without killing them, the ultimate in incapacitation.

There are, however, plenty of skeptics who question the military's use of the term "nonlethal," especially in light of the experience in Moscow. "There is no way known to medical science that can put a large number of people to sleep without killing a sizable percentage of them," says Harvard biology professor Matt Meselson, one of the world's leading experts in arms control and biological and chemical weapons. "In medicine you are dealing with one patient. You can see when he is asleep and, assuming your hand isn't shaking too badly on the valve, you probably won't kill him. But the military objective is different. You have to put 100 percent of the people to sleep—not 50 percent, not 70 percent—and you have to put them to sleep fast. There isn't any way to do that effectively and safely."

JNLWD spokesman Shawn Turner says the military has recently abandoned research on calmatives but not because of international legal issues. "It's really been a matter of budget constraints more than anything," says Turner. "We've looked at calmatives in the past, but we just don't have the funding right now."

Not so, says Edward Hammond, director of the Sunshine Project, an Austin, Texas-based public-interest group that deals with biological and chemical weapons issues. "The JNLWD has been fascinated by calmatives since its inception, and it is chomping at the bit to use them," he says. Under the Freedom of Information Act, the Sunshine Project has obtained a host of interesting Pentagon documents that reveal the Pentagon's deep and continuing attraction to calmatives, including tests on animals and possibly even human subjects. The documents also reveal an internal Pentagon debate on how to get around what is consistently described as the "challenge" of international treaties.

Research on calmatives was discontinued for several years in the early 1990s because of fears that the weapons violated existing international law. Not to be deterred, legal minds in the military came up with two arguments that exploit what they think are loopholes in the treaties, enabling them to restart R&D efforts on calmatives. And the Pentagon has tried to advance its arguments through a vigorous public relations campaign to counter what Pentagon planners have described as the "CNN factor"—media stories that might "elicit such negative public or political reactions as . . . that NLWs violate international treaties."

One Pentagon document, produced after a JNLWD-led joint US and British seminar on calmatives in urban warfare, called on the United States to "continue current efforts to develop and execute a public information campaign plan." This and other documents show an almost Orwellian obsession with language and led to debates on whether to call them "nonlethal" or "less than lethal." Some in the military have even tossed around the term "weapons of mass protection." This obsession with terminology has a lot to do with the fact that the Pentagon's two arguments for the legality of calmatives are essentially semantic.

The first argument involves reclassifying calmatives as a riot-control agent. One Pentagon document from 1999 notes that "calmative and gastrointestinal convulsives, if classified as riot control agents, can be acceptable." Other Pentagon documents suggest shifting the funding for studies of calmatives to the Justice Department or Energy Department to avoid legal problems, and that is just what has happened. A University of Pennsylvania calmatives research project, which was once funded by the Pentagon, is now being underwritten by the Justice Department, furthering the argument that they are being studied solely for use by law-enforcement agencies.

It is a rather transparent smokescreen. The head of one of the studies is the former director of the JNLWD. And numerous documents reveal that the Pentagon has developed a range of weapons capable of delivering calmative chemicals, including specialized bullets, landmines and a mortar round developed by General Electric. "It is hard to see how mortar rounds can be used in domestic law enforcement," notes Harvard's Meselson. Other documents show that Marine Corps officers have received training in chemical warfare doctrine by the JNLWD.

The second Pentagon argument for the legality of calmatives involves the definition of war under existing international law. Sure, incapacitants might be banned during war, goes the argument, but how do you define war? The Pentagon says the term is limited to offensive international war, which would exclude actions like the one in Mogadishu and other "peacekeeping" efforts that seek to enforce international law. Pentagon planners have put this type of mission into the nonwar category of "military operations other than war."

"This is a description that can be applied to every conflict since World War II," says the Sunshine Project's Hammond. And the kind of ambiguous, low-intensity conflict that took place in the Persian Gulf and Mogadishu is just what is depicted in the various scenarios envisioned by military planners laying out appropriate uses for calmatives. One hypothetical scenario for calmative use cited by the Pentagon even involves hungry civilians rioting at a food distribution center.

Incapacitants might be banned during war, goes the argument, but how do you define war?

John Alexander, the former head of the JNLWD and author of *Future War: Non-Lethal Weapons in Twenty-First-Century Warfare*, says such weapons can and should be used in any upcoming military action in Iraq—which would, in most interpretations, put the United States in the ironic position of violating the same international laws that it is ostensibly seeking to force Iraq to comply with.

"If we fight Saddam, there is a high probability this is going to take place in Baghdad," says Alexander, who helped compile a recent report by the National Academy of Sciences that endorsed further work developing calmatives. "You know damn well he is not going to fight us in the open again. That means we are talking about tough urban combat. Imagine what the Russians faced in Grozny. Are we as a nation prepared to send troops into combat knowing that we are going to have very high casualties and also knowing that we have weapons systems like fentanyl immediately available to allow us to do the same things without taking any casualties? It doesn't make any sense to willingly sustain casualties because some lawyer wants to sue you over treaties. The people who support the chemical treaties, they say any violation will bring about the end of the world as we know it. Even if these weapons were prohibited, the truth is we've got the wrong treaties to begin with. We might tap-dance around these questions at the Pentagon and at the NAS, but that is the frank answer."

Not everyone in the Administration agrees with this kind of realpolitik or the Pentagon's semantic dance. One high-ranking official at the State Department who deals with chemical and biological weapons issues was disturbed when confronted with the Pentagon's arguments for the legal use of calmatives. The official, who asked not to be identified, defended the development of calmatives for law enforcement uses but was surprised when told that the military had produced a mortar round capable of delivering a chemical payload. "You apparently have more information than I do," said the official. "This is not something that has come up for a formal intragovernmental review. But I assure you I am going to get to the bottom of it."

Despite the reservations of some, the Pentagon's creative legal interpretations were adopted almost verbatim by an NAS report released last October. The NAS agreed that chemical NLWs should be allowed under "legal interpretations of the [CWC] treaty indicating that it does not preclude such work or the employment of such agents in specified and increasingly important military situations." The report noted that "the Chemical Weapons Convention prohibits

---

Since the Bush Administration took office, it has embraced and expanded on the Clinton Administration's work to develop new forms of anthrax.

---

the development, production, acquisition, transfer, stockpiling, and use of chemical weapons. However, the definition of chemical weapons in the CWC is critical, since it can allow for the use of some NLWs." The report also adopted the Pentagon's Orwellian definition of war, saying that "the United States generally interprets 'means or method of warfare' to mean the offensive use of force in international armed conflict."

In some ways, the military's development of calmatives is part of a larger, disturbing expansion of the country's biological warfare capability. Since the Bush Administration took office, it has embraced and expanded on the Clinton Administration's work to develop new forms of anthrax and the CIA's replication of a Russian germ bomb, according to the 2001 book *Germs* by *Oregonian* managing editor Stephen Engelberg and *New York Times* reporters Judith Miller and William Broad. The Bush Administration has also made it harder to detect violations of current international law by effectively blocking an international draft agreement to create an inspections regime to enforce the BTWC last year. Negotiators from 143 countries had already agreed to strengthen the treaty, which—unlike the CWC and nuclear weapons agreements—has no real enforcement mechanisms. "The Bush Administration's decision to walk away from the draft on the table and to reject any possible future draft was a big mistake," says Elisa Harris, who helped shape the draft when she served as a biological weapons expert on Clinton's National Security Council.

The Administration's decision to back out of the agreement has raised suspicions that Washington itself has something to hide. In the wake of the September 11 attacks, Congress passed $6 billion in funding ostensibly for defensive biological warfare measures. But the line between bio-defense and bio-offense is a thin one. The scientific know-how for both is often identical. And America's premier new bio-defense facility, being built at California's Lawrence Livermore National Laboratory, happens to be right next door to a large fermenter capable of producing biological weapons on a massive scale.

"At every turn, whether we are talking about calmatives or biodefense, we are acting to give the impression that we are involved in offensive biological-weapons development," says CUNY professor Barbara Hatch Rosenberg, who chairs the Federation of American Scientists working group on biological weapons. "This will only encourage other countries to do the same, under the cover of defense, as the United States is doing. We are encouraging a biological arms race. The doctrine of preemption has replaced the doctrine of arms control."

U.S. Troops Find New Uses for Non-lethal Weaponry[3]

By Harold Kennedy
National Defense, March 2002

As the war on terrorism grinds on, U.S. military forces and civilian organizations are finding more and more uses for weapons that don't kill.

Marines guarding the newly reopened U.S. Embassy in Afghanistan, for example, are equipped with non-lethal rounds for their 12-gauge shotguns to drive away unarmed rioters.

U.S. troops overseeing Al Qaeda and Taliban detainees at the naval base at Guantanamo Bay, Cuba, are training to use stingball grenades to put down a prison rebellion.

The Air Line Pilots Association International has called for the installation of stun guns as standard equipment in airline cockpits to thwart would-be hijackers with minimal risk to passengers.

The stun gun is only one of many non-lethal technologies that could be used against terrorists on airliners, Marine Col. George P. Fenton told *National Defense* magazine in a wide-ranging interview. Fenton is director of the Defense Department's Joint Non-Lethal Weapons Directorate, which is headquartered at the Marine base at Quantico, Va., just outside of Washington, D.C.

Some technologies, "predominantly available off the shelf," could be made available in the near term, Fenton said. These include pepper spray, slippery foam and entanglement nets. Other concepts might take longer—three years or more—he said.

For example, a pilot-activated passenger-immobilization system could be developed to incapacitate everybody in the passenger compartment, Fenton said. However, such a system has some risks associated with it, he warned.

For one thing, Fenton said, "chemical incapacitants or immobilizers are not instantaneous." They could take 60 seconds or so to work, and during that time, a terrorist or group of terrorists might be able to do considerable damage.

Also, the infirm—babies, elderly or seriously ill—could be injured permanently or even killed. The policy and legal implications of these risks need further study, Fenton said.

Confusion Abounds

There is, in general, a good deal of confusion about non-lethal weapons, Fenton noted. "People don't understand what they are," he said. "If I had my way, I'd change the name."

It is important to realize that non-lethal weapons can be hazardous to your health, Fenton said. Any weapon that uses force to make you change your behavior—as non-lethal systems do—can

> *Since ancient times, military forces always have had some non-lethal capabilities.*

injure, even kill you, unintentionally, he warned. "I can hurt you with water."

The Defense Department, he explained, defines non-lethal weapons as those "explicitly designed and primarily employed to incapacitate personnel or material, while minimizing fatalities and permanent injury to personnel and undesired damage to property and the environment."

Since ancient times, military forces always have had some non-lethal capabilities, such as use of billy clubs, rifle butts and—in recent decades—tear gas. But all too often, military options in crowd control turned quickly to live fire, Fenton said.

The Pentagon's interest in non-lethal weapons increased sharply in 1995, when U.S. forces helped United Nations troops withdraw from Somalia. Their orders were to do this with a minimum of military and civilian casualties. But they had few non-lethal weapons at the time.

Once, in Mogadishu, "a car blew through a UN checkpoint, ignoring all signals to stop," Fenton said. "The guards opened fire, killing all of the occupants. When they opened the car door, they found a Somali family—father, mother and children."

To minimize such incidents, Marine reservists, who also happened to be Los Angeles police officers, suggested that U.S. military forces try using the kinds of non-lethal technologies employed for years by domestic law enforcement agencies.

Then-Marine Lt. Gen. Anthony Zinni, who was charged with protecting the withdrawal, sought—and received—a quick response to acquire and deploy such technology in Mogadishu, but it received little use.

The following year, however, Marine Gen. John J. Sheehan, then commander in chief of the U.S. Atlantic Command, speaking at a conference in Washington, D.C., charged that "existing weapons development, procurement, training and equipping policies have not kept pace with the emerging needs for non- and less-lethal weapons."

In the CNN era, an individual's decision to use or not to use deadly force is no longer merely a tactical decision, but a strategic one, Sheehan said, because "the implications of the decision will be immediately broadcast to every capital in the world."

In July 1996, the Defense Department established a Joint Non-Lethal Weapons Directorate to develop and employ such weapons throughout the armed services. The Marine commandant was named executive agent for the program, responsible for stimulating and coordinating non-lethal weapons requirements for all services. It is an important assignment, said the current commandant, Gen. James L. Jones.

"Today, world events mandate a need to project non-lethal force across all levels of war to enable our war-fighters and leaders to deal effectively with a host of traditional, as well as non-traditional, threats," Jones said.

The Focal Point

> *"Students learn to discriminate between tourists and terrorists."*
> —Marine Col. George P. Fenton

The directorate has an annual budget of about $25 million and a staff of 21 drawn from the Army, Navy and Air Force, as well as the Marines, Fenton said. "This is the focal point for non-lethal weapons for the entire Department of Defense," he pointed out.

The directorate is responsible for non-lethal concept exploration and program development for all U.S. armed services. The Marines' Non-Lethal Individual Weapons Instructors Course, now located at Fort Leonard Wood, Mo., teaches more than 300 students per year from all the services and several allied nations.

The school is designed to "train the trainer"—produce instructors who will return to their home units and conduct basic user-level training. The school's graduates also often serve as non-lethal operations advisors to commanders. Training includes communications skills, crowd dynamics, unarmed self-defense, riot-control tactics and non-lethal munitions deployment.

Students learn to discriminate between "tourists and terrorists," Fenton said. "Suppose you're on guard on a U.S. warship in a foreign harbor, and a motorboat comes speeding toward you," he proposed. "You only have minutes—maybe seconds—to decide what to do. It would be nice to have an option that would stop the motorboat without killing a potentially innocent driver. That's what non-lethal weapons are all about."

It is also important to remember that non-lethal weapons are not intended to replace lethal weapons, but to provide another option when killing may not be the right choice, Fenton stressed. "We always have our lethal weapons ready," he said. "Non-lethals are a complement, a force multiplier."

Already Deployed to Field

Since 1996, the Joint Non-Lethal Weapons Directorate has fielded:

- Ballistic and non-ballistic body, face and shin shields.
- Riot batons.
- Portable bullhorns.
- High-intensity searchlights.
- Disposable hand and ankle cuffs.
- Stun grenades.
- 12-gauge shotgun shells filled with rubber pellets.
- Flash-bang munitions.
- Pepper spray.

The directorate tries to keep the needs of the combat soldier in mind, Fenton said. "I'm not an acquisition bubba," he said. "I'm an infantryman. I know what it's like to be shot at."

The directorate researches technologies that show promise in crowd control, incapacitating individuals, clearing areas or facilities, and disabling vehicles, Fenton said.

Currently in production, he explained, are 66mm vehicle-launched non-lethal grenades, 40mm non-lethal crowd-dispersal cartridges, and portable net barriers to stop vehicles at roadblocks.

Still in development is an "anti-traction material," a slippery foam that is sprayed on the ground or floor, making it impossible for vehicles or personnel to move.

"I love this piece of gear," Fenton said. "Once you step on this foam, you cannot stand up. Cars' wheels will spin. You just can't get any traction. And what's nice about this is that it's environmentally safe."

Another interesting weapon, Fenton said, is called a pulsed-energy projectile. "It's the closest thing we have right now to the phasers on the television series 'Star Trek,'" he said. "Remember how Capt. Kirk was always saying 'set your phasers on stun?' The projectile works like that."

The projectile's charge—like that of a phaser—can be adjusted to produce a light shock, to stun or to kill, Fenton explained. "The good news is that it works," he said. "The bad news is that, right now, it weighs 500 pounds."

Nevertheless, Fenton said that he is confident that the device is "less than 10 years away from fielding." At first, it is likely to be placed aboard ground vehicles, such as Humvees or light armored vehicles. Eventually, it may be installed on AC-130 gunships.

Another weapon envisioned eventually for special operations AC-130s is the advanced tactical laser, said Fenton. "This is an ultra-precise weapon," he said. "You could take out a column of armor without hurting the refugees along the roadside."

The ATL produces a four-inch spot of energy with a welding-torch effect with a range of up to 20 kilometers, Fenton said. It could be used on a number of aircraft, he said, adding: "I'd love to see this on an Osprey." Development work on the ATL starts in fiscal year 2003, Fenton noted.

The Joint Forces Command is sponsoring an active-denial system, which uses directed energy to repel belligerents without hurting them, Fenton said. "It's like touching a hot light bulb," he explained. "If you were hit with something like that what would you do? You'd get the hell out of there." The actual range of such a system is classified, Fenton said, "but it's in excess of 500 to 700 meters."

The directorate also is investigating the use of malodorous substances in crowd control, Fenton said. "We're looking at things that smell bad—the odors of such things as fecal matter, rotting flesh, natural gas or fermented cabbage," he explained. "We think that smells like that will do a lot to help break up riots." The research, he said, is still in the early stages.

Not all of the technologies examined by the directorate work out, Fenton admitted. For the last several years, for example, researchers have experimented with a material called rigid foam, which could be sprayed around the edges of doorways and windows. The idea was that the foam would harden, sealing the openings shut. "We found, however, that the foam didn't work as well as nail guns," he said.

Also, because the directorate is joint, projects are not pursued unless two or more branches express interest in paying for them, Fenton said.

"The Air Force had a flashlight device that they were interested in, but they couldn't get any other service to support them," he said. "So I said, 'OK, Air Force, you're on your own.' If they want it, they'll have to pay for it themselves."

VI. The Future of Modern War

Editor's Introduction

With each war, technology takes a quantum leap forward. World War II helped usher in both the Atomic Age and the Space Age; after Vietnam, the helicopter became a crucial combat tool; the 1991 Gulf War introduced stealth technology with the F117-A Stealth Fighter. In 2003 the conflict in Iraq saw the introduction of the MOAB (massive ordinance air burst), the most powerful conventional bomb in the world (also referred to by the Pentagon as the "mother of all bombs"). As the 21st century continues to unfold, military forces will again adapt and change with the times, developing new technology and new strategies of engagement. From GPS systems, to pilotless "drones," to language synthesizers not unlike *Star Trek's* universal translator, soldiers of the future will be better prepared for combat than ever before. "Today's spec-ops guy is loaded with everything," military expert Richard Marcinko told this editor. "It's like Christmastime. We're reaching the point now that you can call for help from anywhere. Someone in the Pentagon can push a button and say, 'Well, I just took care of that 6,000 miles away.'" However, Marcinko stressed, this does not mean that the military can rely solely on technology to do the fighting. "It takes training to work the technology, and if you don't have the basics, you're lost," he said. "The technology is there now to extend the natural instincts that you and I have." This section looks at the steps the U.S. military is taking to bring warfare into the future.

"Outfitting the Army of One" by Monty Phan and Lou Dolinar covers some of the new equipment a 21st-century soldier may use. The authors provide a head-to-toe look at the warrior of the future, including night-vision monocles affixed to helmets, stronger body armor and shoulder-mounted weapons that can spot targets at extended ranges. Phan and Dolinar also reveal how the military employs computers, using a system that links an entire unit together on a network. Theoretically, this technology allows for better communication and a reduction in friendly-fire casualties.

Although the concept of "autopilot" is one that has been around for decades, Peter H. King's article "In New Era of War Pilotless Planes Soaring" shows how the military is taking that idea to the next level. An unmanned aerial vehicles (UAV) like the Predator offers many advantages over human pilots, according to the article. For one thing, it can fly longer, higher, and faster, free from the limits of human endurance. In addition, if it were to crash or be shot down behind enemy lines, there would be no pilot to rescue. This feature alone, the article concludes, makes it a more favorable type of weapon to the American people.

"High-tech Gear Making Troops Precise, Deadly" by Michael Hedges takes a closer look at the new technology currently employed by the military. Hedges discusses the 4th Infantry Division, the first brigade to fully employ digital technology to choose targets, relay information, and plot troop movements. He also explains how the Air Force now uses laser- and satellite-guided bombs to strike targets with deadly accuracy. Hedges also shows the next phase of helicopter-assisted combat with the Longbow Apache, a gunship capable of firing 16 missiles in 30 seconds and leaving before an enemy has time to return fire, a maneuver commonly called "fire and forget."

Matthew Brewer's article "Eyes in the Sky" covers the expanding role of satellites in modern war. Not only can they capture detailed images of everything from aircraft to roads, but they can also intercept telephone and radio communications and triangulate the position of targeted individuals who are speaking on cellular phones.

Ian Mount, David H. Freedman, and Matthew Maier have compiled a comprehensive look at the future of warfare in their article "The New Military-Industrial Complex." From high-energy lasers, to SoldierVision, which allows troops to see through walls, to robotic Gatling guns, the authors cover every angle of modern war. In addition, they tell readers what companies will be manufacturing this technology and how much it will cost the average taxpayer.

Outfitting the Army of One[1]

By Monty Phan and Lou Dolinar
Newsday, February 27, 2003

Global positioning systems—the same devices commonly found in today's cars and fishing boats—were used so scarcely a dozen years ago that not even a commanding general of U.S. forces in Desert Storm had one.

"I was somewhat of a skeptic of the utility of a device that would tell everyone where they were, but it took me about a day in the desert to see the value of GPS," says retired Gen. William Nash. He was so impressed, he made sure his officers had them.

But now personal GPS units are commonplace in the military, and high-tech devices from fiber-optic scopes to body armor will be part of the gear toted by American soldiers if the United States goes to war with Iraq. The amount of technology makes the Army's slogan—"An Army of one"—more apt than you might think.

Not all of it involves electronics, either. In fact, the Program Executive Office Soldier—based at Fort Belvoir, Va., and formed by the Army in June—found out the kind of equipment that ground troops in the field really want: waterproof socks.

"If you want to find out what a soldier needs, just go out and ask," says Maj. Andy MacDonald, an assistant program manager of soldier equipment for PEO Soldier, explaining the program's philosophy.

Because of the PEO findings, the Army spent $60 million to outfit five brigades with the latest gear, which amounts to 60 to 120 pounds of equipment for the typical soldier.

From MacDonald's and others' explanations, here is today's techno-soldier, from head to waterproof toes:

Advance combat helmet. The headgear design is similar to a motorcycle helmet, but it can handle more impact, provides better protection and, at 4 to 4 1/2 pounds (depending on size), is a pound lighter than the old helmet, MacDonald says. It also perfectly illustrates the military's mantra, to make equipment lighter but stronger.

Night-vision monocle. The 4-inch-long, 5-ounce cylinder mounts on a helmet and magnifies ambient light, giving a soldier the ability to see when visibility otherwise is limited.

---

1. © 2003 Newsday, Inc. Reprinted with permission.

Navy SEAL Training (Source: www.militaryphotos. net)

Comfortable undergarments. One of the biggest improvements the Army made was supplying soldiers with long underwear, designed specifically to reduce chafing and make the wearer more comfortable, MacDonald says. When interviewing soldiers who had fought in Afghanistan, at the top of many of their lists of requests were clothes that would keep them warm, he said.

MOLLE, or Modular Lightweight Load-bearing Equipment. Designed to replace the rucksack, the MOLLE is tailored to individual soldiers. It also holds a hydration system, a portable water-filled bladder that's connected to a straw-like tube, similar to what bicyclists use. The system replaces the canteen, which took both hands to open. "If it takes two hands to use, then you've got no hands holding the rifle," MacDonald says.

Interceptor body armor. Made by Point Blank Body Armor Inc., a Florida-based subsidiary of DHB Industries Inc. of Carle Place, the Interceptor is a bulletproof vest that is compatible with the MOLLE, allowing for better movement. In addition to the vest— which protects the torso, collar and groin and weighs 8 to 9 pounds—a pair of plates, weighing as much as 9 pounds combined, can be worn for extra protection. "There are soldiers walking around alive today because of those plates," MacDonald says.

Vision enhancers. A military term called "full-spectrum capability" refers to the various vision-enhancement devices used by soldiers. Night-vision equipment is a standard device, but soldiers also use fiber-optic devices, small cameras that allow users to see around corners or through holes in doors.

There are others, too, some of which are light enough to mount on a soldier's rifle. For example, Lexington, Mass.–based Raytheon, the fourth-largest defense contractor, supplies the Army with a thermal weapon sight, which has been in use for about a year and uses infrared waves to detect heat. It mounts on rifles and allows users to see through darkness, smoke, blowing dust and any kind of adverse weather, says Dave Shea, a Raytheon spokesman.

For longer-distance reconnaissance, Raytheon makes what it

For the first time, Americans fighting a war could rely as much on bytes as they do on bullets.

---

calls the JAVELIN Antitank Weapon System, a shoulder-mounted missile-launcher. However, the system, which uses infrared imaging, also has a portable eyepiece that can see targets at extended ranges and is often used for reconnaissance, Shea says.

Col. Don Campbell, who commands the First Brigade in the Fourth Infantry Division out of Fort Hood, Texas, says his soldiers carry a number of vision enhancers, including night-vision devices and thermal-imaging sights. It's one reason the Fourth Infantry Division often is referred to as the "digital division."

GPS Plus. Handheld GPS units combined with two-way radios. It's "two for the price of one," MacDonald says. These two pieces of equipment usually are separate, so combining them reduces weight and bulk, he says.

Satellite phones. Some soldiers will carry the phones, which were in use 12 years ago but not widely available until the advent of the Iridium satellite network, a multibillion-dollar project—funded primarily by Motorola—that the Pentagon helped bail out of bankruptcy in 2000. Tim Brown, a senior analyst at *GlobalSecurity.org*, an Alexandria, Va.–based strategic think tank, said Iridium has some advantages over the military's system: It's cheap, easy to use and makes it fairly simple to set up quick-and-dirty communications networks.

Waterproof socks. These fit nicely into the . . .

Boots. Today's footwear has a soft undersole instead of the harder one soldiers used to wear. It absorbs more shock and is more comfortable, says Maj. Keith Smith, who is based at Fort Benning, Ga., and is a systems manager with the Army's Training and Doctrine Command.

"This is the first time in the history of the Army that the soldier in the field is being treated as a complete system," PEO Soldier's MacDonald says. "We're looking at the soldier and the equipment he's wearing and how it all integrates together."

A Digital Revolution

For the first time, Americans fighting a war could rely as much on bytes as they do on bullets.

Digital technology has revolutionized the U.S. military, to the point that not only will it use devices that were nonexistent when America fought in Iraq 12 years ago, but it has some that weren't even operational in Afghanistan 12 months ago.

"I'd never been to a digital unit, and I would not want to go back to being an analog brigade commander," said Col. Don Campbell, who commands the First Brigade of the Army's Fourth Infantry Division, the so-called "digital division" based in Fort Hood, Texas. "I've been in the Army 24 years, and I've never been in a division that's more combat-ready."

Should America go to war in Iraq, it will mark the first use of the Army's Force XXI Battle Command Brigade and Below, or FBCB2, a system that networks all the combat vehicles in a command, allowing for real-time tracking of units and, theoretically, a reduction in friendly fire casualties, which in the 1991 Persian Gulf War resulted in the death of 35 U.S. servicepeople.

Campbell said the system is mounted in every vehicle, including the tanks, Bradley fighting vehicles, Paladin self-propelled howitzers and Hummers. A screen displays where each unit is, and controls allow users to filter out individual vehicles to get clearer overviews of the battlefield.

Scouts will use the Long-Range Advanced Scout Surveillance System, which mounts on a Hummer and has a laser range finder that can identify objects up to 12.5 miles away, Campbell says. Also in use will be the Unmanned Aerial Vehicles, which were employed in Afghanistan and survey the ground from 6,000 to 8,000 feet in the air.

Of course, any information gleaned from those devices will be fed into the overall network.

"The tests they've run have generally been successful," says author and military historian James Dunnigan. "They're using kids from the Nintendo generation who are very comfortable with this approach."

In New Era of War, Pilotless
Planes Soaring[2]

By Peter H. King
The Los Angeles Times, December 22, 2002

In early November the front page of this newspaper carried a remarkable photograph from Yemen. Taken from television footage, the shot depicted a bearded Yemeni in white robe and sandals, bent at the waist, picking with a stick at a black spot in the desert sand.

The black spot, the caption explained, was all that remained of what had been, moments before, a vehicle packed with suspected Al Qaeda operatives. The car had been hunted from on high by a CIA-operated airplane, which hit it with an antitank missile.

The attack, for many reasons, marked a big day in the war on terrorism, but there would be no medal for the airplane's pilot. This was because there was no pilot. The plane was a drone or, more specifically, a Predator—one in a line of pilotless aircraft being designed and largely handmade here in San Diego by a company very much on a roll.

"Up until September of last year," Thomas J. Cassidy Jr., the head of General Atomics Aeronautical Systems Inc., said last week, "things were kind of flattening out in the world of producing these airplanes. . . . And then all of a sudden 9/11 hit, and everybody started making tons of these things."

Every war produces a signature piece of equipment or two. In the Persian Gulf War, Patriot antimissile systems were an early media darling, only to be replaced at center stage by the Humvee. In Vietnam, of course, it was the helicopter, and in World War II the jeep and the aircraft carrier (and, for that matter, nuclear bombs).

The line can be traced back through the biplanes of World War I, the ironclads of the Civil War, and on and on to the innovative bronze body armor of the ancient Greeks.

Now, with the prospects of war in Iraq looming larger every day, and with the amorphous "war on terrorism" only begun, it would seem to be the time of the drone.

Once-skeptical Pentagon officials have begun to speak of a future in which a third of all U.S. military aircraft are flown by remote control.

Other aerospace companies have begun to gear up to get into the game. President Bush has praised Predators by name.

---

2. Article by Peter H. King from *The Los Angeles Times* December 22, 2002. Copyright © 2002 *The Los Angeles Times*. Reprinted with permission.

And the workshops of General Atomics Aeronautical Systems now fairly hum with activity, as workers in blue and white lab coats mold wings, wire up software, install landing gear, mount missile carriers and generally build almost from scratch Predators and Predator Bs, the latest variation on the design.

"I think we have cranked out 82 Predators so far," Cassidy said, "and we will probably continue to build a dozen a year. And now we are ramping up Predator Bs.

"We've added 300 people to this company, went from 500 to 800, in the last year, just to meet increased demand on production. We have added additional plants and equipment and facilities."

The company was started 10 years ago as an affiliate of General Atomics, a nuclear power contractor.

The owner, Cassidy recalled, wanted to explore the potential of unmanned aerial vehicles, or UAVs: "He kind of told me we need to do this. Go do this."

So Cassidy, beginning with five hires, did.

> *The [pilotless] planes are operated from "cockpits" on the ground hundreds, if not thousands, of miles away.*

"I had been a fighter pilot for 35 years," he said, "and I had been around airplanes all my life. And I knew that a lot of people had tried to do this before, and a lot of big companies had tried it, and nobody had been very successful. I didn't think they went about it the right way."

There were, of course, stumbles and setbacks along the way, but what developed over the decade was an aircraft, roughly the size of a small private plane, that can hover for hours, transmitting by satellite television-like images of battles in progress or targets on the move.

The planes are operated from "cockpits" on the ground hundreds, if not thousands, of miles away. While they can be flown by computer, like commercial airliners on automatic pilot, in clear conditions the on-board cameras make it possible for an operator, half a world away, to fly a Predator as if looking out the window. If there were a window.

In Bosnia-Herzegovina, Predators were first deployed for surveillance missions and later for marking targets. In Afghanistan, they were rigged with air-to-ground missiles.

Eventually, Cassidy said, they could be developed to attack other airplanes and operate from aircraft carriers.

Before his pursuit of the drone, the Bronx, N.Y.–born Cassidy had commanded a carrier-based fighter squadron in Vietnam, served at a high level in the Pentagon and retired from the Navy as a rear admiral. Despite his background, Cassidy has no problem with the idea of forcing pilots to share combat airspace with his drones.

"I think a lot of pilots say, well, why would anybody want to mess with those things?" he said. "But we only use these unmanned airplanes in situations where piloted airplanes have no business being—on very dull and dangerous missions, on very long, endurance missions.

"See, the beauty of these things is that they go to an area and they stay there. . . . A tactical airplane with a pilot has to go out, refuel, go to an area, come out, refuel, go back in, come out. It's just hours and hours of boredom, interspersed with moments of stark terror, as the saying goes.

"With these things, with the unmanned airplanes, there is no terror. They go, they stay, they dwell, they persist. And now that we have weapons on them, we shoot."

Global Hawk flies over Edwards Air Force Base, Calif., during its first flight (Source: www.dod. gov*).*

As demonstrated by the black spot in the sand of Yemen.

Also, should a drone be shot down—and it has happened—there is no downed pilot to rescue from the woods or sea, no prisoner of war to be trotted before cameras. And no body bag to ship home.

"You get a pilot on the ground," Cassidy said, "and it's a big deal. But if one of these airplanes goes down, there is no loss of life. There is no political nonsense trying to get the poor guy out."

Beyond any technical capabilities, this feature alone would seem to make the Predator the ideal U.S. warplane for its time. The Gulf War and Bosnia sold many Americans on the comforting concept of relatively bloodless combat. Push a button, kill an enemy, see it all on TV.

A *Times* poll last week showed that nearly half those Americans who now support sending troops into Iraq would change their minds if American losses were to exceed 5,000. And for these people—who want the war but not the casualties—what better weapon to send into harm's way than a plane without a pilot?

High-tech Gear Making Troops Precise, Deadly[3]

By Michael Hedges
Houston Chronicle, February 23, 2003

Inside each tank and armored vehicle of the 4th Infantry Division now on ships bound for possible war with Iraq is a device that looks like a laptop computer on steroids.

Called the Force XXI Battle Command Brigade and Below, or FBCB2, the computer improves tank operators' ability to keep track of the battlefield.

When commanders want to get an instant picture of where tanks are located on a battlefield, they glance at icons on the computer screen that track the movements of each vehicle. To send an order to hundreds of soldiers, they compose it on the computer and send it to an entire brigade, getting near-immediate responses and confirmation that the order was received.

"We are leaps and bounds ahead of where we were in 1991," said Col. Don Campbell, leader of the division's 1st Brigade, the Raiders. "Whoever our adversary is, he will be very surprised."

Tank operators now can work more effectively at night, with upgraded infrared optics. They have the ability to fire at one target while locking on to another.

Each brigade commander has a drone equipped with cameras that can fly over enemy lines to transmit pictures.

Military planners say those improvements will help them reduce friendly fire, fight in urban settings, and limit the threat of chemical and biological warfare. The changes also have increased firepower.

"We have awesome capabilities," said Col. Dennis Rogers, commander of the division's 2nd Brigade, known as the Warhorse Brigade. "We are the most lethal division on the face of the earth."

The transformation of U.S. armored units since the early 1990s has been matched in other parts of the combat arsenal as aircraft, ships and armor have been upgraded to take advantage of technological leaps.

The tanks, aircraft carriers and planes assembling in the Persian Gulf region look nearly identical to the weaponry used during the war against Saddam Hussein's regime.

But technology has transformed even the most familiar heavy U.S. weaponry. Weapons platforms decades old are more lethal today than their original designers envisioned.

Nowhere is this change more pronounced than with the Army's 4th, the first fully digitalized division whose upgraded Abrams tanks have benefitted from a technological revolution.

Technology also is changing how wars are fought from the air.

"I think to illustrate that, you only have to look at the B-52," said former Maj. Gen. Barry McCaffrey, who led a division into Desert Storm and later served as President Clinton's drug czar.

The venerable Buffalo, as it is called, first flew in 1954. It was designed as a strategic bomber to drop loads of unguided bombs from high altitude.

"Today, that thing is the most effective tactical weapon in the world," McCaffrey said. A B-52 can deliver scores of laser- and satellite-guided smart bombs within a few meters of where they are needed. "The impact of these weapons on the Iraqis is going to be beyond belief," he said.

Some weapons that first were widely used during Desert Storm are more fully integrated into the American arsenal today.

The USS *Harry S. Truman*, now on duty within striking range of Iraq, carries several types of precision-guided bombs capable of being dropped by the Navy's F/A-18 Hornet aircraft.

Weapons platforms decades old are more lethal today than their original designers envisioned.

In the Gulf War, about one U.S. warplane in five had the capacity to drop so-called "smart bombs." Now, every Air Force and Navy strike aircraft can precisely guide bombs.

Apache helicopter gunships were lethal to Iraqi tanks in 1991. But they also had trouble coordinating with ground units and had night-fighting limitations.

The latest version of the helicopter—called the Longbow Apache—is so new it wasn't deployed in the attack on Afghanistan.

It can unleash 16 laser-guided antitank missiles in about 30 seconds, then leave before an enemy can return fire. This capability, called "fire and forget," minimizes the helicopter's vulnerability to groundfire.

Meanwhile, the belief is that the Iraqi conventional forces have gotten weaker since March 1991, strangled by a trade blockade that has denied them spare parts and equipment.

Iraq still has roughly 420,000 soldiers, 2,200 main battle tanks, 3,700 other armored vehicles and 2,400 artillery weapons, according to a study by the Center for Strategic and International Studies, a Washington think tank.

The U.S. troop buildup in the Persian Gulf is approaching 90,000, but it could double within the next few weeks, the Pentagon said last week.

McCaffrey, who commanded the 24th Infantry Division in Desert Storm, said the Iraq figures are deceptive.

Upgrading the Arsenal

Technological advances in the last decade have dramatically increased the
capabilities of U.S. weapons:

- All Air Force and Navy strike aircraft now equipped with precision-guided bombs
- Unmanned aircraft transmit pictures of enemy positions back to commanders
- B-52 now equipped with laser- and satellite-guided smart bombs
- Tanks have better infrared night vision, can fire at one target while locking onto another
- Newest helicopter can fire 16 laser-guided anti-tank missiles in 30 seconds, leaving before enemy returns fire
- Computers allow commanders to track every tank's position, more quickly give orders and receive responses

---

"A few years ago Saddam wanted to threaten Israel by moving two
divisions toward the border with Jordan. So many vehicles broke
down, they never got there," he said. "They have had very poor
maintenance of their equipment."

The main fighting power of the Iraqi army is in six Republican
Guard divisions containing about 50,000 men.

There also is a Special Republican Guard unit of about 15,000 that
is fanatically committed to protecting the Iraqi regime. McCaffrey
said some Republican Guard units probably would fight. "They have
no alternative," he said. "They know that after Saddam is gone, the
Iraqi people will view them as brutal oppressors."

The Iraqis also have about 40,000 paramilitary and militia troops
that could mount guerrilla-type attacks from inside houses and
buildings in Baghdad and other cities.

Iraq still has good air defenses, buttressed by fiber-optic cable sold
to the country by China. U.S. war planners already have locked in
that fiber-optic system as a Day 1 target, a Pentagon official said.

And the Iraqi military has some Scud missiles, more a threat to
civilian centers in Kuwait and Israel than to U.S. forces.

McCaffrey said chemical weapons should not be a threat to U.S.
troops, as long as training procedures are carefully followed.

The Abrams tanks and Bradley fighting vehicles have an "over-
pressurized" system that provides filtered air. That protects troops
from poisons in the air and allows them to fight without wearing
cumbersome anti-chemical weapons suits.

Upgraded versions of the weapons that decimated Iraqi forces in
1991 may not be the only surprise. For months, Department of
Defense officials have hinted at new devices.

Among these may be the high-powered microwave, or HPM. Pentagon officials say it is a device loaded into a cruise missile that can produce an intense surge of energy described as a man-made lightning bolt.

Such a weapon could fry computer motherboards and chips, rendering radar and other communication equipment worthless. They also could create intense, but nonlethal, pain in ground forces, igniting panic.

Asked about HPM at an August briefing, Defense Secretary Donald Rumsfeld said, "You never know. . . . In the normal order of things, when you invest in research and development, you don't have any intention or expectations that one would use it. On the other hand, the real world intervenes from time to time."

Defense Department officials confirmed that war planners had been assessing how to use HPM in a war with Iraq.

The new technologies have not solved all battlefield problems, as witnessed by incidents during the Afghanistan fighting.

One frightening example is the friendly fire deaths in Afghanistan, including the killing of four Canadian soldiers by a bomb dropped by a U.S. aircraft.

American commanders conceded a gap still exists in the goal of allowing aircraft and attack helicopters to instantly identify friendly ground units.

But some antifratricide methods will be used for the first time, including outfitting ground vehicles with a device that will give them a thermal signature that can be tracked.

U.S. Navy SEALs during a Joint Task Force Exercise (Source: www.militaryphotos.net).

On the computer screens inside U.S. tanks and armored vehicles, each companion vehicle will be identified by an icon. That icon can be touched with an electronic stylus, and details about the vehicle will show.

Not all of the new technology has been fully distributed among American forces.

The 4th Infantry remains the Army's only fully digitalized division, although other units have some of the same capacities.

The digitalized M1A2 Abrams tanks of the 2nd Brigade, 4th Infantry Division, are among the relatively few available for use by units bound for Iraq.

Some Bradley fighting vehicles being sent overseas have a radically improved laser targeting system that makes them much more effective at targeting and destroying. But many still have Desert Storm-era systems.

Many of the Humvee light trucks that were ubiquitous in the last Gulf War are a newer model that has been armored to deflect AK-47 rifle rounds and withstand small mines. But others are the more vulnerable version of the early 1990s.

Defense Department officials maintain there is enough of the best equipment to have it focused at the points of attack if American forces are asked to hit Iraqi defenses.

Eyes in the Sky[4]

BY MATTHEW BREWER
AD ASTRA, NOVEMBER/DECEMBER 2001

It sounds like a scene from a Hollywood movie or a Tom Clancy novel. In a godforsaken place in the middle of nowhere, terrorists train how to create mayhem and chaos abroad. Later, in the still of the night, an international attack team from the Coalition moves in, attacking all threats with deadly efficiency and accuracy. They already know exactly who and what is there, and where. The entire raid is watched in real-time from Washington, clear on the other side of the world. Now realize that this isn't a movie, or a novel; it is what can happen today.

It is said that in war, knowledge is power. To this end, knowledge is obtained through many different methods. While Human Intelligence (HUMINT) plays a critical role concerning the thoughts and motivation, a large amount of tactical information is obtained by satellite reconnaissance. In the early days of airborne recon, hot air balloons were used to observe the battlefield. Armed with this knowledge, critical decisions could be made regarding the placement of armament, numbers, strengths, and positions. During the First World War, the balloon was replaced by the more maneuverable aircraft, which continued to be a source of information up to the early 1960s. This view changed, however, when Francis Gary Powers' U-2 plane was shot down in 1960 over Russia. It was then that it became apparent the safest and most reliable position from which to carry out recon was in space in Low Earth Orbit (LEO).

Launched in August 1960, CORONA was the first of 92 American recon satellites put into orbit by 1974. These included satellites such as Argon, Discoverer, Samos, and Lanyard. During the Cold War, these were used to watch over the U.S.S.R. In the early days of satellite imagery, data retrieval was not the quick, efficient system that it is today. To receive the data, it was required to jettison a film canister down from space. This in turn was picked up either via aircraft, or where it landed. In this present age, we have progressed from the film canisters used in the early craft to the near real-time broadcast capability of the Keyhole, Orion, and Lacrosse satellites, and with greater quality images and information.

Today, 40 years after the first reconnaissance satellite was launched, the Cold War is over; now we find ourselves in a new form of war, one which isn't against any single country or power. It

---

is spread out in the hills, valleys, and deserts of the world. In order to locate and deal with these threats, we need to see from above. We once again turn to our eyes in the sky.

A large number of the satellites presently in orbit are considered to be what is referred to as "dual-purpose" satellites, which have a general civilian application, such as oceanography, meteorology or agriculture. While performing their primary tasks, these satellites can also be used in a military aspect, using the same data and images for security matters. To date, these satellites have served a great role in keeping an eye on the activity below, including some of the following events:

- In 1986, images were taken using the SPOT satellite platform to show the location and construction of a chemical warfare plant in Libya. Built as a cooperative effort with the French as a low-resolution platform, the SPOT (Système Pour l'Observation de la Terre) craft is capable of taking images with a 10-meter resolution. This makes SPOT ideal in finding and surveying large camps and groupings of vehicles. The SPOT platforms are currently still in use.

- During the Gulf War in 1991, information was gathered using the Landsat satellite. With the data provided, the Coalition was able to find enemy ground disturbances, and even individual movement of artillery and tanks. Primarily for large targets, the 30-meter monochrome resolution imagery is capable of tracking hostile forces and capabilities, both fixed and mobile. Landsat is also capable of using IR sensors at a 120-meter resolution.

- A Canadian satellite named Radarsat, launched in 1995, was used for night imaging of Burundi during peacekeeping efforts. With synthetic aperture radar imaging instead of optic sensing, the Radarsat is able to give imaging with a 10–100 meter resolution and "see" through clouds, day or night, to supply critically needed information for the peacekeepers.

Of course, talking of the different resolutions is meaningless unless we have an understanding as to what size object can be detected. From space, features in the terrain can be identified at 90 meters. Identification in this case means a general identification of the object, not specific identification. For example, while an aircraft can be identified as an aircraft at 1.5-meter resolution, a precise description of type can be made at 1 meter. Roads can be identified from a 6-meter resolution, while a tank is detectible at 0.6-meter resolution. Left to the naked eye, these items may not be as readily recognizable. With new imaging software, specific details can be enhanced and worked so that the analyst can distill information from each frame.

Reconnaissance satellites are capable of collecting valuable data other than just optical imagery over hostile territory. Unlike the early craft, many the modern systems are capable of using infrared (IR) and broad-spectrum imagery also, instead of straight imaging. This allows the analysts studying the data the ability to make critical decisions and distill information, regardless of the weather at the target's location, and day or night. IR is also capable of detecting heat signatures from both vehicles and people, which can indicate if the subject of the surveillance is about to mobilize.

Yet another task that several reconnaissance satellites can do is electronic eavesdropping. Telephone, cellular phone, satellite phone and radio communications can be intercepted and used for intelligence information. Not only can the contents of the message be learned, but also the location of the person can be traced. Several years ago, a target of the Russian military was known to use his cell phone. Knowing that it could be triangulated, he usually kept his calls below 5 minutes. One time he didn't. The result proved fatal for him.

How does all of this information work to our advantage? With satellite imagery, analysts using computers to enhance pictures

---

Telephone, cellular phone, satellite phone and radio communications can be intercepted and used for intelligence information.

---

can find a base camp. Once it is found, the layout, number of people, and protection can be determined. Also, intelligence concerning the radio and telephone communications can be gathered. If a missile attack is warranted, such as those carried out in the Gulf War, the missiles can be fed data from the satellite, with the best targets and waypoints programmed in. Alternatively, a strike force can be rallied for the assault on the base, with the knowledge of what the manpower and layout of personnel is at the target.

The information gathered can also be used as a bargaining chip to some extent. In the search for terrorists and those who aid them, it is sometimes difficult to determine if a person or organization is set up within the area. With the satellite imagery, the targets can be located and identified. Should a country deny that a person or base is in the country, the data and imagery from the satellites can then be used to refute the claim.

During the present state of unrest, it is reasonable that enemies would want to be able to have access to similar data and imagery. This would allow them to determine what the most current placement of our forces is. Simply put, target data acquisition can work both ways, should the opponent have the finances or backing to provide this information. From this, they could determine what defense would be most effective to repel onslaught, resulting in considerable damage on each side.

While the military is using the images with a range rumored to be less than 0.3 meters, the private sector has begun to fill the market demand for high-resolution imaging. American companies such as Earthwatch and Space Imaging Corp. have filled much of this void, producing images with a reported quality of 0.5-meter resolution. What can be done to keep opposing forces from obtaining this critical data? Several options have been suggested and initiated.

Since June 1978 the American government had kept the image quality at 10-meter resolution maximum, under Presidential Directive (PD)/NSC-37. With the commercialization of improved satellites such as Landsat, however, the restrictions on the images had to be changed. In 1992, a new Presidential Directive was issued, PD-23, giving commercial systems unlimited resolutions, but with a few restrictions.

> *The fact that the information from American satellites cannot be distributed has not deterred some in the Middle East.*

Under PD-23, U.S. companies are now required to keep a log of the taskings of each of their satellites, and give the government access to any and all data obtained. In times where national security, international obligations, or foreign policies may be put into a compromising position, as determined by either the Secretary of State or Defense, the government has the right to restrict data. Some of the other restrictions imposed by PD-23 include putting limitations on the foreign sale of these systems, and the need for the companies to meet eight requirements, including incorporating the ability by the government to encrypt data. Also, images of less than one meter cannot be delivered to a nongovernment customer within 24 hours. This lag in time is to prevent potential targets from learning the positions and capabilities of any forces that may be approaching.

The fact that the information from American satellites cannot be distributed has not deterred some in the Middle East. In 1992 the United Arab Emirates sought to purchase an imaging satellite from a company in the United States. While this was eventually rejected due to PD-23, a Saudi company known as Eirad did eventually purchase equity shares in the Eyeglass satellite, which is now known as Orbview. Presumably these shares allow tasking options for the company.

If you were to wish satellite data on any specific region, it is possible to obtain it at a price. In 1997, the prices for satellite imagery were as follows. An image from the SPOT family of satellites typically sold for $8,000, Landsat approximately $4,000 per photo, and Russian imaging shots cost $3,600 for the film, or $10/km. While these are not enough to give details, it is enough, as we have seen, to give locations, and in some cases, structures.

The United States is not the only country with satellites capable of gathering military information. India, France, Japan, China, Russia and Israel all have platforms that can act in this capacity. Fortunately, these countries have agreements in place in which the release of information is altered, taken at oblique angles, or released at a later time so as to protect friendly assets located in the imaged areas. These countries are not willing to release the data for the same reasons mentioned by the United States; their own security becomes an issue.

What if the enemy has decided to disable our satellites? While we do not have to worry that a satellite will be shot down, due to the altitudes, it is possible to have one disabled. This is possible in several ways. If the opponent has a neighboring satellite, it is possible to hit ours with projectiles, disabling it. During the early days of orbital stations, the Russians had placed on one of their stations a cannon that was capable of rapid firing. It would have been a surprise for the cosmonauts if the kick of the cannon put them into a spin! Needless to say, this addition was not placed onto later craft.

While the satellites wouldn't be physically disabled, NATO understands that they can be disrupted from the ground. During recent U.S. war games, part of the exercise was a supposition that the enemy was using commercial satellites for surveillance. To counter this move, the Army used electronic jamming and lasers to blind the satellite's optic systems. These options are still available, and may be within the arsenal of the terrorists, being well funded at this point. Should this happen, a new alternative for information and data may need to be used.

The International Space Station has been considered to be an information platform. The question arises, however: Should the ISS be used for military activities? The ISS was conceived to be a peaceful, international effort. With an optically correct window in the Destiny module, pictures and data could be taken of the terrain below its orbital route. Using the station for targeting and spying on enemies may not be supported by the other countries, even if they also oppose the offending nation.

With reconnaissance and tactical information coming from space, the high technology weapons will be the newest in this new war. The soldiers on the ground will also benefit from the tactical information given to the leaders from our reliable and all-seeing satellites watching from above.

The New Military-Industrial Complex[5]

By Ian Mount, David H. Freedman, and Matthew Maier
Business 2.0, March 2003

The next time American armed forces go to war—if they're not already fighting in Iraq as you read this—the nature of the battle will be unlike anything the world has ever known. Afghanistan provided a glimpse of the latest generation of high-tech weaponry, but it was only a glimpse. A major assault by combined American forces will provide a full demonstration of the military's new doctrine of faster, lighter, smarter warfare—combat in which cutting-edge technology becomes U.S. troops' deadliest weapon. The Pentagon calls this new doctrine RMA, for "revolution in military affairs," and it's made possible not just by fresh thinking in the Pentagon but also by a subtle shift in the ranks of U.S. defense contractors. In building its new high-tech arsenal, the United States has also created a new military-industrial complex.

The old one hasn't disappeared, of course. Following a round of consolidation during the 1990s, traditional contractors like General Dynamics (GD), Lockheed Martin (LMT), Northrop Grumman (NOC), and Raytheon (RTN) still command large chunks of the funds budgeted for new weapons, which amount to $69 billion in 2003 alone. But the innovation that underpins high-tech warfare comes increasingly from companies that aren't widely known for defense work—or widely known at all. One was originally founded to build nuclear power plants. Another is best known for having once made Mason jars. Brand-name technology companies like IBM (IBM) and Hewlett-Packard (HPQ) have ramped up their defense businesses to provide electronics for some of the military's most sophisticated systems. In a dangerous world, the newcomers' weapons serve a grim, if necessary, purpose. But they also offer further proof of technology's power to change even the most hidebound institutions.

Land

The transformation of the U.S. military has triggered an identity crisis for American ground troops. Though still the first to hit the beaches, the heavily armored forces fielded by the Army and the

---

Marines were largely left on the sidelines during several recent conflicts, as strategists placed greater emphasis on precision-guided munitions and unmanned planes. As speed and stealth take precedence over size and weight, U.S. land forces are modifying their arsenal accordingly.

Tactical High-Energy Laser

One of the biggest duds of the Gulf War was the Patriot antimissile system, which failed to destroy many of the Scuds that Saddam Hussein lobbed at Israel and at U.S. troops. The Pentagon has since teamed up with Israel to try a different approach to disabling missiles: Frying them. The tactical high-energy laser (THEL) locks onto missiles with a swiveling laser projector that looks like a giant spotlight; the heat-generating laser beam causes incoming missiles to self-destruct. In tests, the THEL has brought down more than 25 missiles and even halted an artillery shell. Subcontractor Ball Aerospace & Technologies, a $491 million division of container manufacturer and former canning-jar maker Ball Corp., built the system that keeps the laser locked on targets closing in at 1,000 mph.—D.H.F.
Total Cost: $250 million per installation
Company to Watch: Ball Aerospace & Technologies (BLL)
What it makes: Target acquisition system

SoldierVision

Sci-fi's X-ray vision now has a real-world equivalent. The handheld SoldierVision device emits low-power radio pulses that penetrate walls up to 30 feet away, emitting unique patterns as they bounce off concrete, wood, and human skin. SoldierVision analyzes the patterns to create a color-coded "picture" of a room's contents—unarmed civilians or an ambush, for instance. Built by Time Domain, a Huntsville, Ala., firm that holds patents on several ultra-wideband technologies, the first SoldierVision units were delivered to the Army in October.—M.M.
Cost: $29,500 per handheld
Company to watch: Time Domain
What it makes: Handheld surveillance devices

Stryker Interim Armored Vehicle

The Army's M1 Abrams main battle tank weighs almost 70 tons. But to meet its goal of being able to move a brigade of 3,500 soldiers and their armor anywhere in the world within 96 hours, the Army needs a leaner machine. The Stryker interim armored vehicle will get the job done—for now, at least. At 19 tons, it fits in a standard transport plane. Stryker comes in two main variants: a mobile gun system with a 105mm cannon, and a troop carrier that

can move 11 soldiers at 60 mph for 300 miles. Contractors General Motors and General Dynamics turned to Kongsberg Protech, a small Norwegian defense-technology firm, for the vehicle's weapons station. Kongsberg's system allows troops to fire the Stryker's machine guns and grenade launchers and repair common breakdowns without ever leaving the armored interior.—M. M.
Cost: $1.5 million per vehicle
Company to watch: Kongsberg Protech
What it makes: Weapon control system

Air

The joystick warrior has come of age. The videogame-style air campaigns that dazzled CNN viewers during the 1991 Gulf War were a prelude to the dramatic innovations in precision-guided munitions, stealth technology, and unmanned drones that have come since. The ability to drop smart weapons on enemy forces from the air has now become a signature element of U.S. strategy. For the foreseeable future, it's also likely to provide American forces with a decisive military advantage.

F/A-22 Raptor

The Raptor is an entirely different bird of prey. Designed by Boeing, General Dynamics, and Lockheed Martin, the Raptor's composite-and-titanium construction provides agility and stealth. Twin 35,000-pound-thrust engines can cruise beyond the speed of sound without fuel-guzzling afterburners. The Raptor packs six Amraam air-to-air missiles, mounted internally to avoid disrupting the ultrasmooth profile that hides the plane from radar. The missiles are launched by hydraulic arms that hurl them away from the jet so quickly that the weapons-bay doors pop open for less than a second. The first Raptor squadron won't officially reach combat readiness until 2005, but the planes are likely to make a cameo appearance in any earlier conflicts—including Iraq, if needed—for critical under-fire testing. The Raptor's missile-launching mechanism is made by EDO, which specializes in communications gear and composite structures; the contract could be worth as much as $1 billion over the Raptor's planned 40-year service life.—D.H.F.
Cost: $100 million per plane
Company to watch: EDO (EDO)
What it makes: Vertical ejector for air-to-air missiles

JLENS Anti-Cruise-Missile Radar

Ground-based radar has difficulty seeing cruise missiles that hug the terrain. Airborne radar is better, but there are rarely enough planes in the sky to provide comprehensive coverage. A high-tech

blimp can fill the gap. Properly speaking, the Joint Land Attack Cruise Missile Defense Elevated Netted Sensor is really an aerostat—an unpowered blimp. Some 230 feet long and filled with non-flammable helium, each radar-equipped JLENS floats as high as 15,000 feet. Built by TCom, a Maryland-based firm whose entire business is unmanned airships, some JLENS variants can keep a 3,500-pound payload aloft for 30 days and survive 100 mph winds. Others fit in a truck and require a crew of only two.—D.H.F.
Cost: $130 million per installation
Company to watch: TCom
What it makes: Military blimps

MQ-9B Predator B Hunter-Killer

Since its debut over Bosnia in 1995, the Predator unmanned aerial vehicle (UAV) has been the centerpiece of the U.S. effort to develop robotic weaponry. Predators were originally used only as spy planes, but fitted with a Hellfire laser-guided missile, they've gone on to destroy Al Qaeda targets in Afghanistan and Yemen. Coming soon: the Predator B, which can carry 14 Hellfires or six 500-pound smart bombs. The Predator also can launch swarms of mini UAVs that look like engorged metallic dragonflies. Predators are built by San Diego–based General Atomics, a former nuclear-energy division of General Dynamics that was spun off in 1955.—I.M.
Cost: $7.8 million per drone
Company to watch: General Atomics
What it makes: Unmanned planes

Sea

The days of opposing warships slugging it out on the high seas are probably gone for good. The U.S. fleet is now tailored for coastal, or "littoral," operations, in which ships attack targets on land or in the air. But ships are also taking on an entirely new mission: serving as vital nodes in the Pentagon's information network. Instead of supporting national interests through gunboat diplomacy, Navy vessels increasingly act as floating platforms for the collection and distribution of real-time intelligence.

Upgraded Phalanx MK-15 Close-In Weapons System

The Phalanx is a last-ditch defense to protect Navy surface ships from fast-moving cruise missiles, aircraft, or attack boats. Introduced 25 years ago, the Phalanx is a robotic Gatling gun that sprays a wall of 20mm cannon shells at incoming threats. To contend with smarter cruise missiles and radar-evading aircraft,

Brashear, a Pittsburgh-based optics specialist, created a new image stabilizer for the Phalanx's infrared fire-control system that helped it lock onto a missile skimming over the water at nearly the speed of sound. Brashear lost $100 million in 10 years when it was owned by Swiss defense firm Contraves, but Nextel (NXTL) chairman William E. Conway Jr. bought the company in 1997 and turned it around. Brashear earned $2 million in 2001 on sales of $30 million.—D.H.F.
Cost: $5 million per installation
Company to watch: Brashear
What it makes: Fire-control system

T-AKR Strategic Sealift Ships

One of the best tools in the military's quest for quickness is a floating parking garage. The Navy's new Bob Hope- and Watson-class ships can each carry about 50 tanks and 900 heavy vehicles. Inside, the ships feature seven cargo levels connected by ramps and elevators that greatly speed unloading. Though huge, the ships require a crew of just 26 and sail at 24 knots. Units of General Dynamics and Northrop Grumman built the boats, but the Navy outsources their operation to Maersk Line and Patriot Contract Services. Maersk's five-year contract to run the Bob Hopes could top $400 million.—I.M.
Cost: $200 million per ship
Companies to watch: Maersk Line, Patriot Contract Services
What they do: Ship management and operations

Arleigh Burke–Class, Flight IIA Destroyer

At 509 feet long, the Navy's new Arleigh Burke–class destroyers are small compared with the hulking battleships of World War II. But they pack far more wallop. Called Flight IIA, the new ships carry Tomahawk missiles and minesweeping helicopters, yet their most sophisticated system is the latest version of the Aegis radar, which coordinates simultaneous attacks against ships, submarines, aircraft, and missiles. Most impressive, the Aegis was built largely from commercial technology: 129 IBM and HP computers running off-the-shelf operating systems like HP-UX and PowerMax. By avoiding the IT equivalent of the $300 military-spec toilet seat, the Navy has saved millions of dollars. Northrop Grumman plans to deliver the first destroyer equipped with the new Aegis radar, the USS *Pinckney*, in April 2004.—I.M.
Cost: $900 million per ship
Companies to watch: Hewlett-Packard (HPQ), IBM (IBM)
What they make: Next-generation radar electronics

Space

The weapons here on earth fire the bullets, but the hardware in space steers the battle. Satellite networks allow allied forces to communicate, spy on enemies, and locate friends and foes to accuracies of within a few yards. Without them, many of the U.S. military's most formidable weapons would be useless.

Bandwidth Satellites

The new military devours bandwidth. A single Global Hawk unmanned spy plane needs 500 megabits per second to transmit high-resolution video footage. (That's enough bandwidth to transmit the collected works of Shakespeare in a fraction of a second.) The Pentagon operates two constellations of communications satellites, both of which were built by Lockheed Martin. The government's birds have been overwhelmed by the demand for connectivity, however, so the Defense Department has tapped the commercial satellite industry, leasing capacity from companies that normally beam Disney (DIS) and BBC programming to remote corners of the world. Most of the Pentagon's business goes to Intelsat, a privately held firm that was originally formed in 1964 as an intergovernmental venture involving nearly 150 countries. That has generated some controversy: Among Intelsat's shareholders are potential U.S. foes such as Iraq and Iran.—M.M.
Cost: $200 million per satellite
Company to watch: Intelsat
What it does: Commercial satellite operations

SBR Surveillance Satellite

Conventional spy satellites use high-resolution cameras that can distinguish a Ford Explorer from a Toyota Camry while flying 400 miles above the earth. But the cameras can't tell whether a target is moving, and they're easily blinded by clouds or darkness. The space-based radar (SBR) program addresses those shortcomings with a constellation of 24 high-flying satellites that use radar pulses to track moving objects anywhere in the world, in any weather, and to beam data directly to commanders. Though a full fleet of SBR satellites won't be operational for at least six years, Spectrum Astro of Gilbert, Ariz., has been awarded a contract to design an early prototype. Spectrum specializes in building a satellite's "bus"—its payload-carrying body. Owned by its 430 employees, Spectrum has grown its revenues from $18 million in 1996 to $154 million in 2002.—D.H.F.
Cost: $750 million per satellite
Company to watch: Spectrum Astro
What it makes: Satellite chassis

GPS IIR Satellites

Operated by the Air Force, the Navstar constellation of global positioning system (GPS) satellites is the military's best-known space system. Initiated in 1978, Navstar consists of 27 satellites that provide military and civilian users with extremely precise time and velocity information to pinpoint positions within a few meters. Lockheed Martin's new GPS IIR satellites give Navstar a second civil signal and two super-precise military signals, while also improving overall signal strength. Behind many of the enhanced capabilities is a new waveform generator from ITT Industries, of White Plains, N.Y. The generator boosts the satellites' signals; in conjunction with software that allows the satellite to reconfigure signals while in orbit, the added power makes it more difficult for enemies to jam the GPS network.—M.M.

Cost: $40 million per satellite
Company to watch: ITT Industries (ITT)
What it makes: High-powered amplifier

Network

The central component of the Pentagon's new war-fighting doctrine isn't a weapon at all, but an information network. The military wants to tie together every scrap of incoming intelligence to create a comprehensive picture of the battlefield that can be shared by different military branches or combat units in real time. Achieving that will take years, but the basic theory behind network-centric warfare is simple: When every soldier becomes a part of the network, the network itself becomes more lethal than the sum of its parts.

Pocket-Sized Forward Entry Device (PFED) The PFED is a handheld computer created specifically for use by forward observers—the stealthy scouts who take up positions near enemy lines to coordinate air strikes. The devices are equipped with special software that completes the complex calculations needed to determine the exact position of a target. The PFED stems from a partnership between General Dynamics and Florida-based Talla-Tech, which makes the heavy-duty electronics. Built using many off-the-shelf components to reduce costs and ensure ready availability, the PFED incorporates the motherboard, display, and other electronic parts of an HP iPaq h3900-series PDA.—M.M.

Cost: $2,300 per handheld
Company to watch: Talla-Tech
What it makes: Military handheld computers

Combined Arms Tactical Trainer (CATT)

It takes practice to master coordinated air, sea, and land attacks, but "combined arms" exercises are hugely expensive and can sprawl over thousands of square miles. CATT provides a reasonable substitute, allowing hundreds of soldiers to hone teamwork skills in a network of combat simulators. Occupying a building the size of two football fields, a version of CATT is already operational in Britain, with real-time data links to a similar facility in Germany. CATT can be intensely realistic—tank crews see detailed 3-D terrain through periscopes, and foot soldiers step out of their simulated armored vehicles to fight using a "dismounted infantry" simulator. Sound like a huge videogame? No surprise. Hard-core gamers are already familiar with Quantum3D's high-powered PC graphics cards, but many of the company's most powerful systems end up in CATT.—D.H.F.

Cost: $544 million
Company to watch: Quantum3D
What it makes: Computer image generator

RC-135 Rivet Joint Upgrade

Think of the Rivet Joint as an airborne National Security Agency listening post. Rivet Joint aircraft carry signals-interception technologies that allow the crew of as many as 31 analysts, technicians, linguists, and code-breakers to eavesdrop on the enemy. The Air Force's 17 Rivet Joints are built around Boeing 707 airframes first flown 40 years ago, but the planes have received new electronic systems developed by L-3 Communications. The L-3 upgrades integrate data from the aircraft's avionics, global positioning receivers, Doppler radar, and antenna arrays that reportedly can pick up faint radio signals from 300 miles away; they then channel that information to a series of crew workstations equipped with interchangeable flat-panel displays. The entire RC-135 fleet should be upgraded by 2005.—M.M.

Cost: $31.5 million per aircraft
Company to watch: L-3 Communications
What it does: Electronics upgrades and integration

Bibliography

Books

Alexander, David. *Tomorrow's Soldier: The Warriors, Weapons, and Tactics That Will Win America's Wars in the Twenty-First Century*. New York: Avon, 1999.

Alibek, Ken, and Stephen Handelman. *Biohazard: The Chilling True Story of the Largest Covert Biological Weapons Program in the World—Told from Inside by the Man Who Ran It*. New York: Random House, 1999.

Baer, Robert. *See No Evil: The True Story of a Ground Soldier in the CIA's War on Terrorism*. New York: Crown Publishers, 2002.

Beckwith, Charlie, and Donald Knox. *Delta Force*. Orlando, Fla.: Harcourt, 1983.

Berkowitz, Bruce. *The New Face of War: How War Will Be Fought in the 21st Century*. New York: Free Press, 2003.

Bowden, Mark. *Black Hawk Down: A Story of Modern War*. New York: Atlantic Monthly Press, 1999.

Boyne, Walter J., ed. *Air Warfare: An International Encyclopedia*. 2 vols. Santa Barbara, Calif.: ABC-CLIO, 2002.

Cerasini, Marc. *The Future of War: The Face of 21st-Century Warfare*. Indianapolis, Ind.: Alpha Books, 2002.

Clancy, Tom, Carl Stiner, and Tony Koltz. *Shadow Warriors: Inside the Special Forces*. New York: Putnam Publishing Group, 2002.

Clark, Wesley K. *Waging Modern War: Bosnia, Kosovo, and the Future of Combat*. New York: Public Affairs, 2001.

Cobb, Allan B. *Biological and Chemical Weapons: The Debate over Modern Warfare*. New York: Rosen Publishing Group, 2000.

Crenshaw, Martha, and John Pimlott, eds. *Encyclopedia of World Terrorism*. 3 vols. Armonk, N.Y.: Sharpe Reference, 1997.

Dunnigan, James F. *How to Make War: A Comprehensive Guide to Modern Warfare in the Twenty-First Century*. New York: Quill, 2003.

———. *The Next War Zone: Confronting the Global Threat of Cyberterrorism*. Sacramento, Cal.: Citadel Press, 2002.

Dunnigan, James F., and Austin Bay. *From Shield to Storm: High-Tech Weapons, Military Strategy, and Coalition Warfare in the Perisan Gulf*. New York: William Morrow & Company, 1991.

Dupuy, Trevor N., et al. *Dictionary of Military Terms*. 2nd edition. New York: H.W. Wilson Company, 2003.

Emerson, Steven. *American Jihad: The Terrorists Living Among Us*. New York: Free Press, 2002.

Fowler, Will, and John Norris. *NBC: Nuclear, Biological & Chemical Warfare on the Modern Battlefield*. Herndon, Va.: Brasseys, Inc., 1997.

Gold, Dore. *Hatred's Kingdom: How Saudi Arabia Supports the New Global Terrorism*. Washington, D.C.: Regnery Publishing, 2003.

Haney, Eric L. *Inside Delta Force: The Story of America's Elite Counterterrorist Unit*. New York: Delacorte Press, 2002.

Kushner, Harvey W. *Encyclopedia of Terrorism*. Thousand Oaks, Calif.: Sage Publications, 2003.

Marcinko, Richard. *Rogue Warrior*. New York: Pocket Star, 1992.

———. *Rogue Warrior: The Real Team*. New York: Pocket Star, 1999.

Miller, John, and Michael Stone. *The Cell: Inside the 9/11 Plot, and Why the FBI and CIA Failed to Stop It*. New York: Hyperion, 2002.

Sandler, Stanley, ed. *Ground Warfare: An International Encyclopedia*. 3 vols. Santa Barbara, Calif.: ABC-CLIO, 2002.

Shanty, Frank, and Raymond Picquet, eds. *Encyclopedia of World Terrorism: 1996–2002*. Armonk, N.Y.: M.E. Sharpe, 2003.

Shnayerson, Michael, and Mark J. Plotkin. *The Killers Within: The Deadly Rise of Drug-Resistant Bacteria*. New York: Little Brown & Company, 2002.

Sontag, Sherry, and Christopher Drew, with Annette Lawrence Drew. *Blind Man's Bluff: The Untold Story of American Submarine Espionage*. New York: Public Affairs, 1998.

Steed, Brian. *Armed Conflict: The Lessons of Modern Warfare*. New York: Presidio Press, 2002.

Sun Tzu. *The Art of War*. Mineola, N.Y.: Dover, 2002.

Tucker, Spencer C., ed. *Naval Warfare: An International Encyclopedia*. 3 vols. Santa Barbara, Calif.: ABC-CLIO, 2002.

Pollack, Kenneth M. *The Threatening Storm: The Case for Invading Iraq*. New York: Random House, 2002.

Walsh, Michael J. *SEAL!: From Vietnam's Phoenix Program to Central America's Drug Wars: Twenty-Six Years with a Special Operations Warrior*. New York: Pocket Books, 1996.

Additional Periodical Articles with Abstracts

More information on 21st-century warfare can be found in the following articles. Readers who are interested in additional articles may consult the *Readers' Guide to Periodical Literature* and other H.W. Wilson publications.

Designer Bugs. Jon Cohen. *Atlantic Monthly*, v. 290 pp113–18+ July/August 2002.

Cohen relates how, four years ago, a team of Australian scientists, attempting to develop a genetically engineered virus to combat common pests, stumbled across a mechanism that has the potential to increase the killing power of a number of human diseases. Their findings, published in 2001 amid great controversy, highlight the question of whether technologies intended to improve the world provide terrorists and rogue nations with the means to construct the ultimate bioweapon. According to Cohen, the media's handling of the story muddied a vital discussion about how to gauge the threats posed by natural and engineered bioweapons and how to decide what steps scientists, policymakers, and the public should take. Cohen discusses the implications of the Australian team's discovery and their decision to publish the results.

Would They If They Could? Gary Ackerman and Laura Snyder. *The Bulletin of the Atomic Scientists*, v. 58 pp40–47 May/June 2002.

The authors write that the continuing escalation of violence in the Israeli-Palestinian conflict raises fears that terrorist groups will eventually resort to weapons of mass destruction. Experts are most concerned about the Islamic fundamentalist religious core of terrorist groups such as Hamas, Hizballah, and Islamic Jihad, which interpret their religion as allowing any means possible to destroy "the infidel." According to the writers, in the hands of the fundamentalists, Koranic proscriptions against violence are reinterpreted to justify suicide bombings and other acts, making the religious-based terrorism groups among the most likely to seek weapons of mass destruction, experts believe. Nonetheless, any of these organizations would face considerable technical hurdles before carrying out a plot involving such weapons. The potential for these terrorist groups to deploy weapons of mass destruction is assessed, and the support they may enjoy from state sponsors of terrorism is discussed.

Transforming the Military. Donald H. Rumsfeld. *Foreign Affairs*, v. 81 pp 20–32 May/June 2002.

The U.S. secretary of defense argues that, in order to defend the United States, the Pentagon and the armed forces must alter the manner in which they train, fight, and think. September 11 taught the nation the painful lesson that the challenges of the new century are less predictable than those of the last. Preparing for the future, Rumsfeld insists, therefore calls for new methods of thinking and the creation of forces and resources that can adapt rapidly to fresh challenges and unexpected situations. Rumsfeld says that Americans and their military need to accept changing coalitions, comprehend the need for preemptive offense, and prepare for a new war that may increasingly be waged using nonmilitary measures.

Maneuver Warfare. Eric K. Clemons and Jason A. Santamaria. *Harvard Business Review*, v. 80 pp56–65 April 2002.

According to the writers, maneuver warfare is a philosophy of war developed for today's uncertain combat environment. It is deployed to make an enemy unable to fight as an effective, coordinated whole and recognizes the impossibility of controlling disorder and uncertainty. The seven guiding elements of maneuver warfare are targeting critical weaknesses, boldness, surprise, focus, decentralized decision making, rapid pace, and combined arms, principles that can be applied to business strategy because they have been developed to address conditions that reflect those faced by modern executives. Moreover, the writers say, maneuver warfare's concentration on outflanking a rival, targeting his vulnerabilities, and rendering him unable to analyze the situation can help businesses to achieve a decisive advantage with a minimal deployment of resources. The guiding elements of maneuver warfare are illustrated with examples from both the military and corporate spheres.

Nuclear Missile Defense. Richard L. Garwin and Uzi Rubin. *Issues in Science and Technology*, v. 18 pp5–6 Spring 2002.

Two letters comment on a winter 2001–02 article on national missile defense. The first letter discusses the value of interceptor missiles from a midcourse system. The second letter contends that defensive measures, even imperfect ones, complicate and frustrate the strategies of the aggressor in the case of sea, land, and air warfare and in the competition between missile offense and missile defense.

The Army's Dream Lab. Marc Cooper. *The Nation*, v. 273 p16 December 10, 2001.

Cooper writes that the Institute for Creative Technologies (ICT) seeks to develop the most advanced modeling and simulation technology to train U.S. troops for modern warfare through the use of virtual-reality computer games. A look at the technology ICT uses to train troops is offered.

Army Pondering Alternatives for Tactical Missile Payload. Sandra I. Erwin. *National Defense*, v. 86 p581 April 2002.

Erwin says that the U.S. Army is reevaluating its tactical missile program and exploring options to employ new munitions in an effort to make its long-range precision weapons less costly and more relevant to modern warfare.

Weapons of Mass Destruction. Lewis Simons. *National Geographic*, v. 202 pp2–35 November 2002.

Simons writes that the United States may be the most obvious target for weapons of mass destruction, but the whole world is in danger when nations or terrorists turn to such weapons. He reports that some countries are amassing nuclear bombs, and a few more are working feverishly to acquire their first, but the world may have more to fear from other, less familiar means of attack such as cyberterrorism. The danger comes at a time when the old geopolitical rules seem to have disappeared, and in many ways, the world is more dangerous than at any time since 1945, when the United States first used a nuclear weapon to bomb Japan into submission. Zinovy Pak, director of the Russian Munitions Agency, says that there are mainly local causes of conflict, but because of scientific and technological developments, there are new ways and new weapons to resolve the conflicts.

Lock and Download. Keith Naughton. *Newsweek*, v. 138 pp61–2 October 22, 2001.

According to Naughton, the Pentagon's demand for rapid delivery of high-tech weapons is good news for military contractors. Intent on providing equipment that can locate and destroy the enemy in a matter of minutes, military procurement officers are requesting accelerated shipment of high-tech spy devices, lethal satellite-guided weapons, and sophisticated communications systems. The companies set to benefit, Naughton reports, include smaller players such as L-3 Communications, which makes secure telephone equipment and navigation systems, and established firms such as Raytheon, General Dynamics, and Northrop Grumman. According to Northrop Grumman CEO Kent Kresa, the computer chip will be a dominant feature in future warfare.

How Saddam Happened. Christopher Dickey and Evan Thomas. *Newsweek*, v. 140 pp34–38+ September 23, 2002.

The authors argue that America helped to create the monster that is Saddam Hussein. When Donald Rumsfeld met Hussein on December 20, 1983, he knew Hussein was a murderous thug who supported terrorists and was trying to build a nuclear weapon. At the time, however, America's big worry was Iran, not Iraq. For the next five years, until Iran eventually gave in, the United States backed Hussein's armies with military intelligence, economic aid, and covert supplies of munitions. America did not put Hussein in power, the authors write, but time and again it turned a blind eye to his predations, saw him as the lesser of two evils, or flinched at the chance to unseat him. Successive administrations always worried that if Hussein fell, chaos would follow. The Bush administration is at last prepared to break with him. The writers discuss several possible scenarios that could follow Hussein's fall.

The Plan to Fight Smallpox. Geoffrey Cowley. *Newsweek*, v. 140 pp45–52 October 14, 2002.

Cowley reports that the federal government recently came up with a plan to vaccinate the entire population against smallpox within ten days of a terror attack, but the inoculation debate is not over. The odds of a smallpox terrorist attack are impossible to gauge, but there is no question that Americans are vulnerable, according to Cowley. Anyone vaccinated before 1972 may still have some residual protection, but the 119 million Americans born since then are defenseless. Health and Human Services secretary Tommy Thompson has presented the White House with a plan that could result in routine "pre-attack" vaccination of up to 10 million health and emergency workers by early 2004. Not yet policy, Cowley writes, this proposal is simply an option that the president will consider as he contemplates his next move in the "war on terror." If the threat of a smallpox attack could be quantified, the vaccine's hazards could be weighed against those of an outbreak, and the debate over vaccination would be winnable. Without that knowledge, Cowley contends, it would be difficult to justify a peacetime vaccination drive.

The Fighting Next Time. Bill Keller. *The New York Times Magazine*, pp32–7+ March 10, 2002.

In a cover story, the writer discusses the work of Arthur Cebrowski, a retired U.S. Navy vice admiral who has been appointed as the head of the new Pentagon Office of Force Transformation. Secretary of Defense Donald Rumsfeld has given Cebrowski the job of revolutionizing the American military and countering criticism that its system, constructed to cope with the cold war, is not suited to the modern world. Keller writes that the Bush administration's version of transforming the military appears to consist mainly of purchasing a great deal more of the high-tech weapons that ostensibly succeeded in Afghanistan, without giving up any traditional weaponry. Cebrowski favors "network-centric warfare," which means hooking together ships, aircraft, satellites, and ground forces to create a detailed, shared picture of the battlefield in motion. This approach, Keller says, makes war more about the chase than the kill. It also ensures that the most important asset on the battlefield is a sensor rather than a weapon.

New Test Could Speed Bioweapon Detection. Robert F. Service. *Science*, v. 295 p1447 February 22, 2002.

Service explains how Park et al., in this issue, report on the fabrication of simple electronic chips that are able to detect DNA from anthrax and other organisms in minutes. In the new technique, target DNA is detected by using it to link fixed "capture strands" to "probe strands" that are attached to current-bearing gold nanoparticles. According to Service, this system seems to be considerably more sensitive than other high-speed detection methods, and, in contrast to many such tests, it does not depend on the PCR, which can be difficult to conduct and occasionally introduces undesired errors.

On Biowarfare's Frontline. Martin Enserink. *Science*, v. 296 pp1954–6 June 14, 2002.

Enserink reports that researchers at the Army's biodefense laboratory have been pulled out of their isolation amid the recent heightened fears of bioterrorism. The U.S. Army and Medical Research Institute of Infectious Diseases (USAMRIID) and the FBI are now working closely to unmask whoever sent the anthrax letters in 2001. The expertise built up by the USAMRIID has proved invaluable and has pulled the research institute out from the intellectual backwaters and into the mainstream.

Better Killing Through Chemistry. George Musser. *Scientific American*, v. 285 pp20–21 December 2001.

Musser writes that chemical weapons can easily be produced and dispersed by terrorists, according to organic chemist James M. Tour of Rice University, Houston, Texas. After being told that federal agencies closely monitor all potential weapons materials, Tour ordered all the chemicals required to make the nerve agent sarin from Sigma Aldrich, one of the U.S.'s most reputable chemical suppliers. The following day, he received enough ingredients to make 280 grams of the toxin. Nerve agent experts agree that such chemicals have to be watched, especially since, given the events of September 11, some of the barriers that were thought to hinder a gas attack, such as the need for the terrorists to get away safely, no longer seem so daunting.

Nuclear Reactions. Daniel G. Dupont. *Scientific American*, v. 287 pp17–18 August 2002.

According to Dupont, a report that the Pentagon is considering the use of nuclear interceptor missiles has stirred controversy. *The Washington Post* recently ran a piece asserting that Secretary of Defense Donald Rumsfeld had permitted the possible use of nuclear-tipped interceptors in the national missile defense system. The Pentagon maintains that it is not looking at nuclear interceptors; however, Republicans in the House lauded the Pentagon's examination of alternatives to current missile defense plans, including nuclear interceptors, as prudent. Dupont writes that House Democrats think it is a bad idea and indicative of a willingness on the part of Republicans to erode the long-standing tenets of U.S. nuclear policy.

Supergerm Warfare. Michael Shnayerson and Mark J. Plotkin. *Smithsonian*, v. 33 pp114–26 October 2002.

In an excerpt from their book *Killers Within: The Deadly Rise of Drug-Resistant Bacteria*, the authors write that drug-resistant bacteria are one of the greatest threats to humankind. They offer evidence that the number of disease-causing bacteria able to fend off the most commonly prescribed antibiotics has grown significantly and that the blame lies with doctors who prescribe antibiotics unnecessarily, patients who do not finish their course of treatment, and farmers who overuse antibiotics to boost livestock growth. An excerpt from Plotkin and Shnayerson's book examines ongoing research into powerful natural compounds that some animals secrete to fight off infections, substances that might help in the development of the antibiotics of the future.

Will Spyware Work? Hogan, Kevin. *Technology Review*, v. 104 pp43–7 December 2001.

Hogan discusses how, despite the most advanced intelligence-gathering technologies in the world, the United States missed a band of terrorists that plotted within its borders. For several decades, electronic systems have been silently established to intercept satellite communications, tap phone calls, monitor e-mail and Web traffic, and then turn this immense flow of information into intelligence reports for U.S. leaders and investigative aids for law enforcement. Hogan points out that, despite the $30 billion invested in their development and the enormous secrecy surrounding them, government information technologies could not detect the World Trade Center plot. Critics claim that the bureaucratic and technical fragmentation within the U.S. intelligence community goes toward explaining how terrorists could hatch their plan under the government's radar.

The Technology of Megaterror. Richard L. Garwin. *Technology Review*, v. 105 September 2002.

Distinguished nuclear physicist and longtime presidential adviser Richard L. Garwin discusses the terrorist threats America still faces. Biological warfare agents are the greatest menace to the country, but not all such agents are the same. Bioweapons perfected by the leading powers in the immediate postwar period included diseases of plants, animals, and humans. These were further divided into infectious diseases, which can be contracted only by direct exposure to a weaponized bacterium or virus, and diseases that are both infectious and contagious. Garwin contends that the May arrest of Jose Padilla also highlighted the threat of "radiological dispersal devices," or "dirty bombs," devices that use explosives or other means to disperse solid or liquid radioactive materials.

That's Militainment! James Poniewozik. *Time*, v. 159 March 4, 2002.

According to Poniewozik, the military-entertainment complex is the new coalition in Hollywood. The networks need a new twist on reality TV, and the Pentagon needs to find a way to maintain public interest in a war that could stay on simmer for years. The symbiotic answer, the writer says, is to send reality TV to war. Last week, ABC announced *Profiles from the Front Line*, which intends to tell the personal stories of soldiers in Afghanistan, the Philippines, and beyond. VH1's tentatively-titled *Military Diaries* consists of over 60 soldiers with cameras who will record their days and talk about how music helps them cope. On March 29, CBS debuts *AFP: American Fighter Pilot*, which follows three F-15 pilots through training.

Why Suicide Bombing Is Now All the Rage. Amanda Ripley. *Time*, v. 159 pp32–9 April 15, 2002.

Ripley reports that dying to kill has become a noble calling among Palestinians, and the practice has gone from being extreme to becoming mainstream. April 16 marks the ninth year since 22-year-old Sahar Tamam Nabulsi, acting on behalf of the militant group Hamas, filled a white Mitsubishi van with cooking-gas canisters and drove into two buses, killing himself and another Palestinian and wounding eight Israelis. Since then, the Palestinian suicide bomber has evolved, and 105 such bombers have gone on to kill 339 more people. According to Ripley, it has become normal and even noble among Palestinians for promising young men and women to kill themselves in pursuit of revenge and the dignity it is thought to bring: Palestinians currently celebrate the suicides in newspaper announcements that read like wedding invitations. Bombers also earn cash bonuses and health benefits for the family members they leave behind.

How Al Qaeda Got Back on the Attack. Michael Elliot. *Time*, v. 160 pp26–27+ October 28, 2002.

Elliot writes that Al Qaeda may have dispersed in the wake of the fall of the Taliban in Afghanistan, but the group is still capable of striking against America and its allies. With the destruction of Afghan training camps, the network has decentralized and many militants have returned to their homelands. These militants have radicalized local groups such as Jemaah Islamiah, which is being blamed for the recent atrocity in Bali. The Bali bombing, Elliot says, is part of a larger spasm of violence that has counterterrorism officials preparing for more strikes. In addition, Al Qaeda training camps are appearing in Pakistan, and U.S. military intelligence believes that Al Qaeda has built the new camps intentionally small so as not to provoke a clampdown from Pakistan's government.

Nukes You Can Use. Mark Mazzetti. *U.S. News & World Report*, v. 133 p40 July 22, 2002.

Mazzetti reports that the Energy Department is seeking to construct a nuclear weapon that is tailor-made for the battle against terror. The Bush administration's new military strategy contemplates preemptive first strikes—and even the remote possibility of using nuclear weapons—against rogue nations such as Iraq. In order to eliminate targets out of the reach of conventional weapons, Mazzetti writes, the Pentagon wants to develop a nuclear bomb that is capable of hitting bunkers that conceal chemical or biological weapons.

Wrecking the Intifada. Ahmad Al-Rubai. *World Press Review*, v. 47 pp18–19 December 2000.

Al-Rubai argues that those who are committed to supporting the Intifada and who advocate the use of violence against civilians outside the Israeli-occupied territories are in error. Any act of terrorism against foreign civilian institutions, he says, is an act that wrecks the Intifada's cause and gives Israel the upper hand in terms of propaganda . The Intifada has achieved great political success so far, according to Al-Rubai, but action taken outside the occupied territories and against civilians will change the focus to side issues, possibly creating a situation of enmity with nations other than Israel and turning global sympathy away from the Palestinians.

Index

For
reference

Not to be taken
from the room.